Clavius

Maginus

Longomontanus

Tycho

Walter

Deslandres

Regiomontanus   Pitatus

Purbach

Straight Wall   Mare   Mare
Nubium   Humorum

Arzachel

Alphonsus   Gassendi

Albategnius

Ptolemaeus

Grimaldi

Eratosthenes   Copernicus
Kepler

The
Apennines   Oceanus Procellarum

Timocharis

Archimedes   Aristarchus   Seleucus

Mare Imbrium

Sinus
Iridum

Plato

Mare Frigoris

Anaxagoras

D1266149

PICTORIAL GUIDE TO THE MOON

DINSMORE ALTER

Director Emeritus

The Griffith Observatory

Los Angeles

PICTORIAL GUIDE

TO THE MOON

Updated and Expanded Edition

Thomas Y. Crowell Company   New York   Established 1834

BY THE AUTHOR

Pictorial Astronomy
    (with Clarence H. Cleminshaw and John G. Phillips)

Pictorial Guide to the Moon

Copyright © 1967, 1963 by Dinsmore Alter
All rights reserved. No part of this book may
be reproduced in any form, except by a reviewer,
without the permission of the publisher.
Designed by Laurel Wagner
Manufactured in the United States of America

L. C. Card 67-18396
2 3 4 5 6 7 8 9 10

523.39
A 466 p

PREFACE

It is important that each reader realize the purpose for which any book on a scientific subject was written. The principal purpose of this book is to provide to the public that information which they must secure if the space plans to which our government is committed are to attain successful results. In a nation where the majority of citizens can veto policies, it is very difficult to embark on those policies which are entirely different from any which the world has attempted previously. Every effort must be made to carry the truth about such matters to the voters.

A secondary purpose of certain chapters is to present data which may assist students of physical science toward decisions regarding which of the current and maybe contradictory hypotheses may more closely resemble the truth as we shall see it after years of study on the actual surface of the moon. Today any dogmatism about these "guesses" would be foolish. At any time new data may be obtained which will change a man's opinion. A scientist must be loyal to data and subordinate his most cherished beliefs to them.

15272

CONTENTS

1 EARLY OBSERVATIONS OF THE LUNAR SURFACE

The next decade is likely to see one of the most momentous scientific achievements in history: man's arrival on the moon. The new era in human endeavor signaled by that event—the age of physical exploration of the moon—will be but the latest chapter in the age-old story of man's relation to his environment. For the moon has always been there, hanging disarmingly close in the clear sky, dominating man's consciousness almost as powerfully as the sun. Its luminous presence, its beauty, and its manifest regularity of movement made the moon loom large in mythology long before it became the object of man's first efforts to observe and understand worlds beyond his own. In ancient legend, and even today in primitive parts of the world, the moon has been feared, loved, revered, and worshiped.

Sometimes the moon was considered a woman, perhaps the mother or the wife of the sun. Or it was a man or a male spirit, perhaps so potent in its maleness that a young woman could become pregnant from drinking the moonlit water upon which the lusty god had cast his light, as some of the Eskimos thought. Or the moon and the sun were ancestors of the human race, or relatives in perpetual conflict. Sometimes the legends became almost lyric in their poetic impulse, as when the Peruvian Indians conceived that the moon had given the gift of silver to the race of man in the form of its tears. All such legends had a common basis in mystery: the moon was intriguing precisely because it was quite unknowable. Centuries passed before the curious and rational Greek mind began to consider the movements of the heavenly bodies and attempted to reconcile the solar year with a year made up of lunar months. Thales of Miletus, the first of the Greek philosophers, is said to have produced the first important calendar reform around 600 B.C. His successors worked out various ways of harmonizing the solar and lunar cycles, but it was not until 45 B.C. that Sosigenes, upon the order of Julius Caesar, stabilized the year on the basis of the solar cycle alone.

It was the Greeks who discovered that the moon is not itself luminous but shines by the

1

reflected light of the sun. And one of the greatest of the Greek scientists, Aristarchus of Samos, made scientific history in the third century B.C. when he combined geometry, ingenuity, and some necessarily crude observations to determine the relative distances from the earth to the sun and the moon, and the relative sizes of the sun, moon, and earth. This was the first scientific attempt to measure astronomical distances; for the first time man began to understand the physical insignificance of his world. Aristarchus concluded that the sun was twenty times as far from the earth as the moon, a value that must have seemed wildly improbable to him, although the actual distance to the sun is 400 times as far as to the moon. His determination of the moon's diameter was remarkably good; he found it to be one third the diameter of the earth, while the true figure is somewhat more than a quarter. He figured the solar diameter to be seven times that of the earth. The true figure is 108 times, but even his figure was an astounding discovery for his century.

Most of the Greeks believed that the earth was fixed in space, with the sun, moon, and planets moving around it. Pythagoras considered the idea. Aristarchus began to conceive and elaborate a theory of the earth's motion, but Aristotle opposed the idea, as Hipparchus did later. Much later still Ptolemy, in his great book, *The Almagest*, crystallized the idea of a fixed earth. The smothering influence of Aristotle and Ptolemy continued almost unabated through medieval times.

Despite the Greeks' remarkable application of scientific techniques to the study of the moon, the moon itself remained quite unknown in any detail—an object of ingenious and romantic speculation. Both the essential change in outlook and the necessary instruments were far in the future.

The third great phase of man's relationship to the moon did not appear until a radical revolution in human outlook was under way. Gradually as the medieval world evolved into the modern era, and the metaphysical interpretation of life yielded bit by bit to the humanistic and scientific interpretation, man came to believe that he could by his own effort understand and even influence his environment. Great new reservoirs of human energy and imagination were released,

and remarkable discoveries proliferated. The characteristic achievement of modern times, the scientific and mathematical analysis of physical nature, was exemplified by the work of Galileo in the seventeenth century. Galileo's contributions to astronomy were based on one of the most significant inventions in the history of science: the telescope. The origins of this device are lost in the obscurity that has frequently enveloped the most pivotal early inventions, but the name of Hans Lippersheim, a lens maker in Middleburg, Holland, is often associated with the discovery. Lippersheim, about the year 1608, found that by combining two lenses in proper positions he could make distant objects appear larger.

The news of this invention soon passed beyond the Alps. Its implications were immediately apparent to Galileo, who constructed his own telescope in Padua during the following year. On a night in June of 1609, a memorable date in the history of human endeavor, Galileo turned his crude instrument toward the moon and the planets. The next year he published, in *Siderius Nuncius*, the results of his first detailed lunar observations. Although his telescope was very simple and disclosed little detail, Galileo's book included a crude map of part of the moon. It also included his determination of the heights of the lunar mountains, calculated by the timing of the first and the last sunlight on their tops.

Figure 1. Galileo's map of the moon. The large crater is probably Copernicus.

Figure 2. One of Hevelius' maps, from his classic *Selenographia*.

Everyone who has seen a mountain peak bathed in sunshine and watched it for a time will remember that the sunlight continues to flood the top peaks for a time after the lower parts of the mountain are in darkness. The same thing happens on the moon, only the effect there is more conspicuous because of the lack of air. With his telescope Galileo could see these lunar mountain tops; the lighted peaks appeared almost as stars close to the terminator, which is the name given to the boundary between day and night on the moon. He observed the time when the starlike peak vanished and measured the distance from it to the terminator. The calculation of height then became merely a problem in trigonometry. (This method is reasonably satisfactory, although observational errors are impossible to avoid, even today, and they make the resulting heights inaccurate.) The values Galileo obtained were somewhat too large but still were useful. Galileo also noted that because of the tilt of the moon's axis to its orbit as it revolves, an observer on the earth sees slightly different parts of the moon's surface at different times.

3

This phenomenon, called libration in latitude, is discussed in Chapter 3.

Observations similar to those of Galileo were made at about the same time by his rival Christoph Scheiner, a professor at the University of Ingolstadt. His work was published in *Rosa Ursina* in 1626, but the book was devoted principally to solar observations and contained no lunar maps. Between 1620 and 1640 Langrenus, a cartographer to the King of Spain, mapped the moon and named some of its features. He is said to have engraved thirty maps of parts of the moon, but the names he used were never widely accepted and his work attracted less attention than it deserved.

Hevelius, whose long and distinguished ca-

Figure 3. A map from Riccioli's two-volume work.

reer spanned much of the seventeenth century, published his great *Selenographia* at Danzig in 1647. In it he rejected the names given by Langrenus and proposed others on the basis of assumed terrestrial similarities. Except for six of his designations, his nomenclature was not permanent, but his maps were better than any produced for another century. One of these is reproduced here.

It will be noted that on this map north is printed at the top, just as on terrestrial maps, instead of at the bottom as on more modern lunar maps. This was the custom in the early days of moon mapping because the first telescopes used the type of eyepiece devised by Galileo, which produces an image right side up. In later and more efficient telescopes additional lenses would be required to produce an erect image, entailing a loss of light as well as extra expense. Since it is immaterial to the astronomer whether the image is erect or inverted, the extra lenses have been omitted and the resulting maps conform to the inverted image. Now that man is actually preparing to visit the moon, engineers working on space travel are beginning to use the erect image on their maps once again.

The maps of Hevelius show a great deal of detail very accurately. Almost uniquely among early maps, they show the areas of the moon's surface that are visible only part of the time because of the libration in latitude. The construction of these maps required many hours of careful observation with awkwardly mounted telescopes. The highest magnification Hevelius used was about forty diameters, and he estimated positions merely by eye. He discovered the moon's libration in longitude, the additional area seen at the east or west of the moon, although he gave an inaccurate explanation of its cause. The periods of the moon's rotation about its axis and of its revolution about the earth are equal while the rate of rotation is constant. The rate of revolution varies during the month because of the eccentricity of the moon's orbit. As a result sometimes the rotation gets ahead of the revolution but lags at other parts of the orbit. The resulting libration in longitude has a maximum value of a little less than eight degrees. Hevelius also measured the heights of some of the lunar mountains, obtaining more accurate values than Galileo had earlier by the same method.

Four years later Hevelius' friend, Riccioli, published a two-volume work. Probably many of the observations used by him were actually made by his associate at the University of Bologna, Grimaldi. Although Hevelius' work is generally rated as the more important of the two, Riccioli's is in some ways superior. It was he who set the pattern still followed in giving names to lunar features, and in the process he demonstrated a good insight into human nature. Although most of the craters were named after great scientists and other historic figures, Riccioli also honored politicians and others of his own generation whom he wanted to please. One of his maps is illustrated here.

Although astronomers following Riccioli performed much valuable work on the moon's orbit and librations and its relations to the sun and the stars, no outstanding cartography was produced for 125 years, aside from the excellent map of Cassini in 1692. In 1775 there was published posthumously the lunar map of Tobias Mayer, a professional map maker at the University of Göttingen. This work was the best of its kind for half a century: as late as 1837 Mayer's micrometric measurements of the positions and sizes of lunar markings were considered authoritative and useful. Mayer's chief fame, however, came from his investigations of the lunar orbit.

J. H. Schroeter published his first volume of lunar studies and observations in 1791 after nearly 30 years of systematic observations with reflecting telescopes made by Herschel and by Schraeder. Magnification ranged from 150 to 300 diameters. The largest of these, with a mirror 19 inches in diameter, was a truly impressive instrument for that time. Instead of using the micrometer to record the positions of lunar objects, Schroeter worked with the less accurate but more rapid "camera lucida." This consists of a special eyepiece for the telescope with a white screen divided into squares mounted below it. The observer looks with one eye through the telescope and with the other at the white sheet; the brain superimposes the two images, and one can trace rapidly what is visible in the instrument.

Schroeter was the discoverer of what he called "rills," and are now often called "clefts." These are long, narrow valleys in the surface, some of them more than a hundred miles long. About 2,000 of them have been mapped to date.

Schroeter believed that he had discovered evidence, through twilight observations, of a lunar atmosphere, a subject which is considered in detail in Chapter 2. He was also the first to introduce a relative scale for measuring the brightness of lunar features.

Schroeter was followed by two Germans, Wilhelm Beer, a banker, and Johann Heinrich von Mädler, a professional astronomer. Their *Mappa Selenographica* and their book *Der Mond* were published in 1837, and their description of the moon was the basic reference work for many years. It is still of great interest to professional astronomers and amateur lunar specialists. Such subjects as eclipses, the moon's path, and its rotation are discussed at the beginning. There are long tables of measurements of the latitude and longitude of lunar markings. Lists of various names given to the same features are included, as are determinations of the heights of many of the lunar mountains. Today the uncertainties in these measurements are understood, but the data were accepted for a long time and are still some-

times quoted. The authors presented evidence (which is no longer accepted) for the existence of a thin lunar atmosphere. A special chapter, signed by Mädler, considered lunar effects on our terrestrial weather. It was a long time before the controversy aroused by this subject finally evolved into a certainty that there is no such influence. The bulk of the book described lunar features in detail.

Almost forty years later, when Edmund Neison published his comprehensive treatise in selenography, he referred to *Der Mond* as "the only work on the subject" and predicted that for many years to come all who followed his distinguished predecessors would have to incorporate the results of Mädler's seven years of observations. But most of the material in Neison's book was new, the result of eight years of constant selenographic observation. This work was done mostly with a six-inch equatorial telescope, and included several hundred sketches sent to the author by other observers, notably by the Reverend T. W. Webb. Neison defended the thesis of a lunar atmosphere very strongly, associating it with the phenomenon of weathering and commenting that "the entire evidence we possess on this subject is strongly favourable to the moon actually possessing such an atmosphere."

Two years before Neison's book appeared there was published in England a quite different book by Nasmyth and Carpenter. It was much less important than Neison's work, but it is perhaps the most beautiful of the standard treatises. The illustrations are so excellent that the unique work of the authors in preparing them should be told in their own words, as an illustration of the highest kind of scientific devotion and craftsmanship:

"During upwards of thirty years of assiduous observation, every favourable opportunity has been seized to educate the eye not only in respect to comprehending the general character of the moon's surface, but also to examining minutely its marvelous details under every variety of phase, in the hope of rightly understanding their true nature as well as the causes which had produced them. This object was aided by making careful drawings of each portion or object when it was most favourably presented in the telescope. These drawings were again and again re-

Figure 4. Title page of *Der Mond*, by Wilhelm Beer and Johann Heinrich Mädler. Published more than a century ago, it is still of interest to selenologists.

Figure 5. A section of a map by Schmidt of Athens. It shows Clavius.

peated, revised and compared with the actual objects, the eye thus advancing in correctness and power of appreciating minute details, while the hand was acquiring, by assiduous practice, the art of rendering correct representations of the objects in view. In order to present these illustrations with as near an approach as possible to the absolute integrity of the original objects, the idea occurred to us that by translating the drawings into models which when placed in the sun's rays, would faithfully reproduce the lunar effects of light and shadow, and then photographing the models so treated, we should produce most faithful representations of the original. The result was in every way highly satisfactory and has yielded pictures of the details of the lunar surface such as we feel every confidence in submitting to those of our readers who have made a special study of the subject."

Most of their book is devoted to the marshaling of arguments in favor of a special form of volcanic hypothesis. The authors made skillful use of the physics of their day, and although much of their discussion has not stood the test of later research, a book of this quality must never be ignored.

The best map of the moon made during the pre-photographic days was the 72-inch one by Julius Schmidt (Schmidt of Athens). The map was published in 1878 by the Prussian government. During the latter part of the nineteenth century, photography began to supplement visual map making although some work of the visual type still persists usefully. The first fifty pages of Walter Goodacre's *The Moon*, published privately in 1931, contains an excellent historical outline.

Throughout the centuries there has been controversy over the proper names given to lunar features. As has been noted, names were first assigned by Langrenus. Then came Hevelius' nomenclature and a few years later Riccioli's. Beer and Mädler standardized the names and added many new ones. Neison adopted their list but added still more, for a total of 513 proper names. In 1878 Schmidt of Athens added about 50 more. In many cases, and particularly in the earlier years, favoritism and politics dictated some of the choices, to the credit of otherwise obscure persons and the detriment of famous scientists. In 1932 the International Astronomical Union standardized the nomenclature by formal acceptance of a report by Mary A. Blagg and K. Mueller.

This outline leads us to the "modern" era of lunar observations which may be considered (rather vaguely) as beginning with the systematic observations by Dr. J. H. Moore and Mr. J. F. Chappell, using the 36-inch refractor of the Lick Observatory as their camera. Some earlier photographs were fully as good as their best ones, but their systematic practice between the years 1937 and 1946 gives their series preeminence. It was the custom at the observatory on nights when the "seeing" was unusually steady and the moon was available, to call these observers. They made several exposures during an hour, then turned the telescope back to the regular observer of the night.

Among the selenographers worthy of consideration during the latter part of the nineteenth and the early part of the twentieth century are: W. R. Birt of England (1804–81); Moritz Loewy of France (1833–1907); Henry Draper of the United States (1837–82); T. G. Elger of England (1838–97); Hermann Klein of Germany (1844–1914); Julius Franz of Germany (1847–1913); S. A. Saunder of Cambridge, England (1852–1912); N. S. Shaler of Harvard (1841–1906); William H. Pickering of the United States (1858–1938); Johann Krieger of Germany (1865–1902). Some of these men were professional astronomers; others were amateurs, but all loved the moon.

7

2 GENERAL CONDITIONS AT

THE MOON'S SURFACE

If the beachhead of the first lunar landing is to be enlarged, if humans are to use the moon wisely and successfully, man will have to accustom himself quickly to a wondrous new environment. There will be dangers without precedent in terrestrial life—and, surprisingly, certain factors of assurance and safety that are absent on the surface of the earth. But all of these things, the good and the bad alike, will be only details in the vast strangeness of an existence to which all the millennia of the human race afford no parallel.

THE DAY ON THE MOON

Life on the moon will completely disrupt one of the most profound and deeply ingrained of man's environmental rhythms—the alternation of day and night, of light and darkness, in a 24-hour cycle that governs work, eating, and sleep. On the moon wondering humans will observe that the circuit of the sun in the heavens, from one dawn to the next, will require the equivalent of 29.53 terrestrial solar days. The schedule of human activity will no longer be related to the external, astronomical clock to which all his existence has accustomed man. No one can predict with assurance what effect this will have on the human body or psychology. Perhaps man's physiology, reflecting the inheritance of unnumbered generations, will still demand the terrestrial working day. It may be that a cycle of shorter periods will better satisfy the needs of the organism. Perhaps, on the other hand, the human body will be adaptable to longer periods of work because of a number of environmental changes. For example, the weight of the body and hence the effort required for various exertions will be much less; the artificial atmosphere provided for human use will be different; food will probably have to differ considerably from the customary terrestrial diet.

Even the appearance of the heavens by day and by night, the progression of phenomena across the sky, will be strange. The sun and the stars will move very slowly in their paths. The earth will be visible, great in size and in clear detail, but its apparent motion will be either slight or spectacular depending on the point on the moon's surface from which the observation is made. From the point that appears to us to be the mean center of the moon's disk, the earth always will appear very high above the horizon. Oscillations in the earth's motion will appear to be at a minimum in this case, but for an observer stationed at certain positions near the limb (the edge as seen from the earth) of the moon, the earth may rise and set, sometimes climbing almost 16 degrees in a very irregular manner, moving sideways in one direction and then the other before it begins its descent to the horizon. From other points near the moon's limb the earth will barely rise above the horizon before dipping back out of sight. The earth will be seen rising at various points on the horizon, depending again on the position of the observer along the limb.

TEMPERATURE CHANGES

The moon's lack of air, which will require man to provide his own atmosphere as a condition of survival, will produce another dramatic consequence in strong contrast to terrestrial conditions. On the earth, weather is a complicated product of very involved processes in which temperature, winds, tides, and atmospheric conditions are the controlling factors. On the moon, weather is mathematically predictable for any designated time, even far in the future. The only relevant factors are the time of day, the position of the observer on the moon, the state of the moon's librations, and its distance from the sun; and all of these are ascertainable and foreseeable for any time and place.

As a matter of fact, the temperature of the surface rocks on the moon has already been measured with moderate accuracy from the earth, a quarter of a million miles away. The chief instrument in the process is an extraordinary device so tiny that hundreds of them together weigh no more than a split pea. It is called a thermocouple and is really nothing more than two very fine, short wires of different materials fused together. The wires have been generally of bismuth and an alloy of bismuth and tin.

Any radiation—such as that contained in a beam of light—that falls on the junction of these tiny wires causes the wires to emit a very small but measurable electric current. The current can be measured by a galvanometer connected to the open ends of the wires; the size of the current gives the intensity of the heat contained in the light beam or other radiation.

The thermocouple cannot be enclosed in glass because glass is opaque to much of that part of the heat radiation which is in the infrared range. The radiation, therefore, usually is exposed to the junction of the thermocouple through a polished rock salt window. Surprisingly, the smaller the thermocouple, the better it performs. As its size is decreased it becomes more definitive, responding to the light from only a small part of the moon's disk, measuring more precisely the heat from a more exact source area. And the smaller the device, the greater is its surface area in respect to its mass; the radiation it receives therefore raises the junction to a higher temperature, increasing the electric current and permitting more accurate measurement.

This instrument was used with signal success by Pettit and Nicholson, and later by Pettit alone, with the 100-inch Hooker telescope at Mount Wilson and smaller telescopes. They followed the subsolar point (the point on the moon's surface with respect to which the sun is at the zenith) across the moon's disk during fifteen consecutive terrestrial nights. In the course of these experiments Pettit and Nicholson encountered several problems inherent in the nature of the radiation they were attempting to measure.

The first of these is that there is a tendency toward what is called specular radiation and reflection. That is, the surface of the moon behaves much as a convex mirror does in reflecting light: too much radiation comes toward us when the subsolar point is at the center of the visible disk, and too little when it is near the limb. The result is a wide variation in the electric current stimulated by the radiation, and this must be corrected for.

Second, the energy that reaches us from the moon's light consists of two parts, and these must be separated in order to make temperature determinations. One part is the radiation from lunar rocks heated by the sun; it is this energy that the observer wants to isolate and measure. He must separate and eliminate the second part: the portion of the sun's radiation that is reflected directly from the moon to the earth instead of being absorbed and heating the moon. This second part is quite independent of the temperature of the reflecting rocks on the moon. Fortunately the radiation from the lunar rocks—the radiation we seek to measure—is in the infrared range, longer in wavelength than is nearly all of the radiation from the sun, and separation of the two components on the basis of wavelength is a purely mechanical procedure.

Finally Pettit and Nicholson found that the tables indicating the amounts of radiation absorbed by the earth's atmosphere, a phenomenon for which due allowance must be made, were incorrect. They were forced to make new tables based on their own experiments.

After struggling with these various areas of difficulty, Pettit and Nicholson finally determined that the moon's temperature at the subsolar point is 101° Centigrade, or 214° Fahrenheit. This result corresponded well with the theoretical value.

The temperature thus determined is subject, however, to very wide variation at other points on the moon's surface. Observations of the temperature near the limb, instead of at the subsolar point, have been made during total eclipse. These observations indicated a drop from 69° C (156° F) to −98° C (−146° F) during the first partial phase of the eclipse. During the time of total eclipse the temperature at the limb dropped slowly to −116° C (−177° F) but it rose to nearly the normal value before the eclipse had completely terminated. This great range of temperature in so short a time indicates that the moon absorbs very little of the radiation falling on it. Only a very thin surface layer is warmed materially. The temperature on the night side of the moon, which of course faces earth during the crescent phase, has been found to be −155° C (−247° F), but this value is subject to considerable uncertainty because the thermocouple produces only a tiny current at extremely low temperatures.

These measurements have recently been checked and confirmed by Sinton, working at the Lowell Observatory with more delicate sensors. He has established isotherms (lines joining points of equal temperature as on a conventional weather map) and has found, in addition, certain variations in temperature that result from the nature of the surface in local areas.

The enormous range of temperature on the moon and the quick progression from one extreme to another will pose a large problem in self-protection for the first humans attempting to cope with these unprecedented conditions. But there is at least one advantage: the high daytime temperature should make the problem of power supply almost unbelievably simple. The temperature of the subsolar point is just above the boiling point of water as we know it at the earth's surface. Water tubes, blackened to cause maximum absorption and mounted in cylindrical reflectors, may be exposed to the direct radiation of the sun for the equivalent of two terrestrial weeks without interruption. These tubes need merely be mounted on axes parallel to the moon's axis of rotation, and then turned at the proper speed to match the moon's rotation. Water or any other convenient fluid may be used—if the adjective "convenient" can apply in reference to a process that may require the transportation of all fluids through a quarter of a million miles of space! The steam produced by heating the water tubes will, of course, have to be repeatedly condensed and later reheated to conserve the precious fluid. The sun would thus act as a perpetual source of fuel for lunar steam engines at practically no cost after initial installation—a possibility that does not, at least at present, exist on the earth.

Solar batteries can also be used advantageously in the clear, airless lunar sky to change solar radiation directly into electrical energy. Although they are not yet capable of delivering heavy current, their development is barely in its infancy, and rapid progress has already been achieved. It is certain that devices of this kind will have valuable uses in lunar scientific laboratories, and we can hope that they will prove to be the best source of current for general use.

A third source of power is either atomic fission or fusion. Atomic engines would be needed at night when sources dependent on solar energy fail, unless adequate storage batteries can be developed.

ATMOSPHERE

The question of a lunar atmosphere was the subject of lively discussion for 250 years, after Adrien Auzout pointed out, during the latter part of the seventeenth century, that if the moon had an atmosphere there should be twilight. This should be most easily visible as a faint light extending a short distance into the unlighted part of the moon. It was more than a century before any astronomer claimed to have observed such an effect. Schroeter announced the discovery after observing the moon as a very thin crescent, at which time the effect should be most noticeable. He determined that an atmosphere sufficient to produce this effect would have to be a trifle more than one mile in height. The moon crosses this distance in its orbit in less than two seconds of time, making observation of any effect of atmosphere very difficult. Today Schroeter's results are known to have been merely illusory.

If there is a lunar atmosphere, the instant of contact of a total solar eclipse should be changed because of the refractive effects of the atmosphere. That is, an atmosphere would form an outside envelope that would bend light and change the moon's apparent size and the position of its limb. Leonhard Euler observed the eclipse of 1748 and decided that the moon does have an atmosphere with a horizontal refraction of 20 seconds. (The earth's atmosphere has an index 102 times as great.) Unfortunately Euler neglected the effects of irradiation. The French astronomer Du Sejour attempted to remedy this defect in Euler's reasoning at an eclipse sixteen years later. The resulting refractive value was only 0.5 second, which gave to the moon an atmosphere with a density $\frac{1}{1,400}$ that of the earth's.

A star is said to be occulted when the moon passes between the earth and the star, temporarily cutting off the star's light as observed on the earth. At the moment such an occultation occurs, the lunar atmosphere, if there were any, should produce three effects: a change in the color of the star, a dimming of the star and its disappearance from view a very brief time later than the predicted moment of invisibility, and its re-emergence into view the same short time

ahead of schedule. The reason for these variations in the predicted times of disappearance and reappearance is, again, the bending, or refraction, of the star's light as it passes through the moon's atmosphere, so that it comes to our eye either later or earlier than it would if it had followed a straight line, unaffected by atmosphere. A few observations of such phenomena were reported long ago by capable, reputable astronomers. In general, however, these results were not verifiable and most astronomers of the nineteenth century reported that no observable effects existed. Even if we were to assume the accuracy of Du Sejour's eclipse results, it is questionable whether any such effects would be great enough to be noticeable at stellar occultations.

The great landmark in speculations concerning lunar atmosphere occurred in 1860, when the famous English physicist James Clerk Maxwell published his monumental *Kinetic Theory of Gases*. Maxwell's work established that the moon could possess no atmosphere of more than negligible density.

Maxwell assumed that a gas is composed of individual particles moving at random. The pressure of a gas on its container is determined by the number of particles that strike a given area in a given time, and by the average kinetic energy of these particles. This energy of motion is the heat contained by the gas. The speed of the particles of gas, therefore, varies with the temperature: at absolute zero the particles would not move at all; at low temperatures they move slowly and at high temperatures they move very fast. Maxwell applied the laws of probability to the random movements of gas particles and worked out the relationships between pressure, temperature, and the speed of the particles in his theory.

What happens in a mixed gas composed of various kinds of particles? As the particles dash about they collide with one another and rebound like millions of billiard balls in endless agitation. The collisions transfer energy from the more energetic particles to the less; the result is an "equipartition of energy," a strong tendency for all particles to have the same amount of energy. Since kinetic energy is a function of mass and the square of velocity, the lighter particles must move faster than the heavy ones.

Specifically, the velocities of the particles will be inversely proportional to the square roots of their masses: if one molecule has four times the mass of another, its speed will be only half as great.

At any one time some molecules of a given mass will have more energy (and thus higher speed) than the average of their kind and others will have less. But the tendency to approach equality makes it possible to determine the average velocities of the particles in a gas at any temperature. The following table shows the average speeds of some particles at 0° C (32° F) and at 100° C (212° F). The first part of the table lists some individual atoms. But in most gases the particles are composed of two or more atoms joined together, and the second section of the table gives the velocities of four such molecular gases.

Table 1

Element	Atomic weight	Speeds in km/sec at	
		0° C	100° C
Hydrogen	1	2.62	3.06
Helium	4	1.31	1.53
Carbon	12	0.76	0.88
Nitrogen	14	0.70	0.81
Oxygen	16	0.66	0.77
Neon	20	0.58	0.68
Argon	40	0.41	0.48
Molecules other than atomic			
H_2	2	1.84	2.15
H_2O	18	0.62	0.72
O_2	32	0.46	0.56
CO_2	44	0.39	0.46

These molecular velocities have a direct bearing on the question of a lunar atmosphere because an atmosphere must be held in place, so to speak, by a gravitational force. Now, a gas molecule moving directly away from the surface of the earth and not striking anything requires a velocity of 11.188 kilometers per second to escape completely from the earth. Under similar conditions on the moon a speed of only 2.38 kilometers would be required. A glance at the speeds shown in the table would suggest that only hydrogen could escape from the moon,

and that there should, therefore, be a considerable atmosphere of the other elements—even including hydrogen in combinations such as water vapor. But we must remember that the values in the table are average speeds. As a result of deviations from the averages, some molecules move quite fast enough to escape if they are not stopped by an encounter with other particles. In a very short time (as measured on the scale of planetary development) almost all of the lighter atoms in any lunar atmosphere would have escaped into space. In any event, the moon can hardly have had much of an atmosphere at any period of its existence.

The heavier of the chemically inactive elements, such as xenon and krypton, exist only as a very small percentage of the terrestrial atmosphere; a lunar atmosphere composed exclusively of them would have an extremely low density. However, unless there be outside interference, such an atmosphere must exist.

Recent observations of space conditions near the earth's orbit, made from artificial satellites, have revealed the presence of streams of very rapidly moving protons that have been termed a "solar wind." Mariner II, in December 1962, has shown this wind to exist far from us. If the moon had a moderately strong magnetic field, as does the earth, these ionized particles would have little effect on any lunar atmosphere. The lunar surface would be protected from them. But, although observations to date have not given positive proof, it appears that if the moon has a magnetic field at all it is very weak. If this is true the "solar wind" sweeping past the lunar surface during eons of time, striking atmospheric molecules and accelerating their motion, would surely have stripped the moon almost bare. This stripping effect is indicated also by radar measurements of the density of the lunar atmosphere, which indicate a measured density of 10^{-13} times the surface density of the earth's atmosphere. In other words, the density of our atmosphere, according to this research, is ten trillion times that of the moon! Even allowing for the maximum error we can conceive, a lunar atmosphere in the ordinary sense of the word must be almost nonexistent.

Yet there remain some bothersome observations tending to suggest an "atmosphere" effect. Three centuries ago, Hevelius reported that markings on surface features of the moon were sometimes less bright and less regularly defined than at other times, although the earth's sky was just as clear. No thin atmosphere such as is conceivable on the moon could possibly account for such obscuration. But similar observations continue to be made in certain lunar areas and at certain times of the lunar day. They are too well authenticated to be ignored.

These observations are perhaps best confirmed within the crater or ringed plain known as Plato, and on the left part of the floor of the walled plain Alphonsus. Goodacre sums up the observations of Plato under three headings.

1. The darkening of the floor from the time the sun is 20° above the horizon until afternoon. Actually the floor does brighten, but to a lesser extent than do the features around Plato.

2. Variations in the visibility of the light spots and streaks without relation to the solar altitude.

3. Occasional obscuration of easily observed features as though by fog. This takes place even though adjoining parts of the moon are seen clearly. Neison reported an observation in which the whole interior was obscured by fog at sunrise. Klein observed a fog-like effect in 1878. R. Hodge, observing Plato near sunset, could find no trace of craterlets. Goodacre confirmed this obscuration by his own observations three hours later. These are merely a few samples of such observations.

There is nothing surprising about such reports of what appears to be a local haze. There is no known reason why there should not be some residual volcanic activity involving the leakage of very low density gases from some of the lunar craterlets. Such gases could have an obscuring effect at the moment of their escape although they could not form a permanent atmosphere. Recent observations have suggested that some such very slight effect is quite probable. (The matter is discussed in some detail in Chapter 16.)

CHANGES ON THE MOON

From time to time observers have reported "changes" on the surface of the moon. Changes of various kinds are certainly theoretically possible, but it is questionable whether, during the past two centuries, permanent changes large enough to be observed from the earth have occurred. ("Fogs" of the kind already described are an example of temporary changes.)

The moon is certainly bombarded by meteorites, just as the earth is. But not even a meteorite crater on the moon as large as the famous one in Arizona could be observed in any detail from earth. Slippages from steep cliffs, triggered by meteoritic bombardment, may have occurred, but, again, probably not on a scale large enough for terrestrial observation during the short time we have had telescopes.

Optical effects probably explain most of the "changes." Everyone who has done a modicum of lunar observing is aware of complete changes of appearance with the altitude and direction of the sun, even small changes in altitude sometimes producing marked variations. A return to the same phase of the moon may not necessarily bring the sun to the same altitude. Librations vary the altitude by a dozen degrees. In addition to this difficulty, many suspected changes are based on old observations. Beyond this there is a psychological factor that influences everybody; it is easy to accept the exciting explanation instead of the prosaic but probable one.

One should certainly keep an open mind regarding permanent observed changes, but the writer is very skeptical about them, except perhaps for residual volcanic activity in the craterlet Linné. Even there it appears probable that varying amounts of haze have produced the observed data. Any reader who wishes to pursue the subject in more detail should read the monograph by Walter H. Haas, who is a very capable and enthusiastic student of the surface of the moon. Appended to it is a bibliography of 83 references.

ALBEDO

The albedo is the ratio between the light which the moon reflects and the light that falls on it. The moon reflects from ordinary parts of its surface only about one-fourteenth of the incident visible light; in other words its albedo is low. A minor cause of this low albedo is the roughness of the surface. The most important cause is the fact that the greater part of the surface is composed of rather dully colored material. There is, however, a very great variation in the albedo of the different features. This is shown conspicuously by the fact that the waning moon, just before the half moon phase, gives us about 20% less light than does the corresponding phase of the waxing moon. The obvious reason is that the lighted area of the waning moon happens to include a greater proportion of the dark plains, called maria. See Plates 3–1 and 3–2.

The angle between the general surface and the line from us to that surface also affects the amount of light we receive. Hence, the albedo cannot be determined at the full moon phase alone because of the tendency toward specular, or mirror-like, reflection. If the moon were a smooth, perfectly polished globe we would receive light from only one spot. Even as it is, the brightness increases very rapidly during the couple of days preceding full moon and falls off very rapidly after that phase has been passed. Although the illuminated area turned toward us at the half moon is half as great as at the full moon, we receive only about a ninth as much light, primarily because of this mirror effect.

In addition to albedo and phase, the distance of the moon from the earth helps determine the amount of light we receive. As an object is moved farther away the angle it subtends (i.e., its angular diameter) is reduced. The angular area varies with the square of the distance. When the moon is closest to us it is only 221,000 miles away; half a month later its distance is 253,000 miles. On account of this variation of distance, one full moon may be 30% brighter than another. Visually, the full moon gives us, on the average, a little more than $\frac{1}{500,000}$ the light we receive from the sun. Photographically, it is even less bright, because of the general slight yellowish tinge of its surface. Part of this tinge, however, is spurious and is due to two non-lunar factors. The first of these is the effect of the earth's atmosphere, which, in screening the light coming through it, absorbs the short, bluish wavelengths more effectively than it does the longer, reddish ones. The second is the greater sensitivity of the normal human eye to the medium (yellow) wavelengths than to longer or shorter wavelengths.

SCALE OF BRIGHTNESS

The albedo of the moon varies enormously from feature to feature. Schroeter devised a scale from 0 to 10 to record the brightness. This was somewhat modified by later observers, and especially by Beer and Mädler. The scale is now defined as follows:

Table 2

0	Black—the dark shadows
1	Grayish black
2	Dark gray
3	Medium gray
4	Fairly light or yellowish gray
5	Light gray
6	Approaching grayish white
7	Grayish white
8	White
9	Glittering white
10	Dazzling white

The interpretation and application of such a scale is obviously difficult for even a moderately experienced observer. Many areas blaze out near full moon and appear of entirely different brightness relative to other parts. Perhaps the best training for the serious student would be to read Neison's description of each feature and to compare it with his own observations.

The following table of brightnesses is taken from Neison. (When "walls" or "interior" is mentioned, the reader must not assume that there are no parts of these which are not much brighter or darker than the average values stated.)

Table 3

Feature	Brightness
Maria	
Imbrium	
general	2¼ to 3½
Sinus Iridum	2¼
streaks	4 to 5
Nubium	2 to 3
Oceanus Procellarum	2 to 3½
Serenitatis	
central	3 to 3½
border	1½ to 2½
Tranquillitatis	1½ to 3

Feature	Brightness	Feature	Brightness
Craters, Ringed Plains, etc.		Kepler	
Alphonsus		walls	7
central peak	7	floor	6
Anaxagoras		Linné	5½
wall and interior	7	Manilius	
Archimedes		wall	8
floor, dark parts	2½	interior	4
light parts	3½	Philolaus	7
east wall	5	Plato	
Aristarchus		walls	6
central mountain	10	floor near	
interior, craterlet and		half moon phase	3
second peak	9½	just after full moon	1+
Aristillus		Posidonius	
interior	3	general interior	3½
Aristoteles		Ptolemaeus	3½
walls and floor	4	principal interior crater	7
Arzachel		Riccioli	
walls	4	floor	1 to 1½
Biot	8	Timocharis	4
Copernicus		Tycho	
floor	3 to 4	general interior	5
slopes	5 to 6	central peak	8
crest	8	base of exterior slope	3
certain peaks	9		
Eudoxus			
interior	3		
wall	5		
Gassendi			
central peaks	6		
Grimaldi			
floor	1		

The present scale of brightness is decidedly better than nothing but it is inadequate for modern research. A suggested plan for creating a new and acceptable scale is outlined later in the book —in Chapter 16.

3 IDENTIFICATION OF LUNAR FEATURES

Features on the moon are located on maps, just as features are on the earth. The making of lunar maps and their use is called selenography. Almost all maps of the earth are drawn, but there are two types of lunar maps. All the famous old books of maps discussed in Chapter 1 are filled with drawn maps, to which were added detailed descriptions of the features. The latest of such books, by Wilkins and Moore, is the last in the distinguished line that began before the middle of the seventeenth century. Maps of this kind describe far more surface detail than can be found in any other source.

The other method of lunar mapmaking is by the use of photographs. These have the great advantage of absolute "accuracy," which cannot be achieved on a drawn map. But this "accuracy" is a tricky thing and considerable experience is needed in the proper interpretation of photographic maps. The tyro is likely to be much surprised and disheartened by the difficulty he experiences when he goes from map to telescope.

The principal reason for this failure of agreement between lunar maps and personal observation is the great variations in shadow which, as the moon's phase progresses, change the appearance of most lunar features by unbelievable amounts. Consider one of the finest lunar objects, the great ringed plain called Eratosthenes. When the sun is rather low in the lunar sky, this plain (Plate 7–5) is highly conspicuous and exhibits a great deal of interesting detail. But at full moon, in the full blaze of reflected light (Plate 7–3) it can scarcely be seen! The cause is the smallness of variation in the reflective quality of its rocky surface, so that shadows are required if it is to be seen well enough to study. The ray system of the neighboring crater Copernicus is an example of the opposite type of change. Under a low sun Copernicus is little more spectacular than is Eratosthenes and its system of rays is difficult to observe. At the full moon, however, Copernicus and its rays stand out with explosive grandeur, and, along with the ray system of Tycho, rival the maria for pre-eminence. Many hours of careful observing are necessary before the observer can avoid the pitfalls inherent in these apparent changes of the lunar surface. Even skilled selenographers have been known to make embarrassing mistakes.

For the purposes of this book, any depression below the surrounding surface (except for those depressed areas that we designate as maria, valleys, or rills) is defined as a crater, a term that includes even many shallow depressions probably due only to the accidental shaping of an area. At our distance from the moon it is often impossible to distinguish these from true craters. The latter may be large or small and circular, oval, or polygonal. They may further be divided into two categories designated as "explosive" and "non-explosive." Those large depressions that for generations have been called mountain-walled plains comprise nearly all the important non-explosive craters. If any explosions occurred during the formation of these walled plains they were apparently merely secondary or "trigger-ing" events. (Such features are the subject of Chapter 11.) The explosive craters, on the other hand, were apparently caused by either volcanic activity or impact of some kind. (They are described in Chapter 12.) The explosive craters have been divided, classically, into ringed plains, craters, craterlets, and crater pits. There are many hybrids among the craters that exhibit both non-explosive and explosive factors in their formation; these should be classified according to which cause apparently was the more important. Alphonsus is an excellent example of such a hybrid.

The true craters can also be divided on the

Figure 6. Libration in longitude. The orbit of the moon is an ellipse with the mutual center of the mass of earth and moon at one focus. Because of the small mass of the moon, that point is only 3,000 miles from the center of the earth. We call the line that connects the center of the earth to the center of the moon, at any given instant, the *radius vector*. Newton's law of gravitation demands that this line sweep over equal areas each second of the month. Consequently when the line is short, the moon must move faster. Consider a month that happens to begin when the moon is at *P*, closest to the earth. Because of the short radius vectors the moon will move all the way to *X* in the first quarter of the month. The arrow represents some lunar feature that is directly toward the earth when the moon is at *P*. The moon turns on its axis only a quarter of the way around by the time it reaches *X*. Therefore we see the arrow displaced. By the time the moon reaches *A*, the arrow is again toward the earth. When the moon is at *Y* the arrow is seen from the earth as displaced to the other side from what it was at *X*. When the moon gets back to *P* at the end of the month, the arrow once more is toward us. The eccentricity of the moon's orbit is exaggerated in this diagram to make the displacement at *X* and *Y*, or libration, easily visible. Also we neglect the small angle between the planes of the moon's orbit and its equator. That neglected angle produces the libration in latitude (see Figure 7).

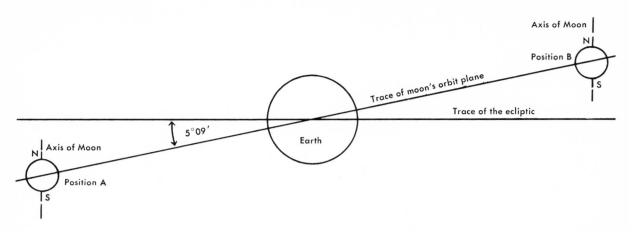

Figure 7. Libration in latitude. The observer is looking at the earth-moon system from a point out along the line in which the plane of the ecliptic intersects the plane of the moon's orbit. From this position the traces of both these planes are straight lines. The angle of 5°09′ between them is purposely exaggerated to make the libration more noticeable. The axis of the moon's rotation is almost perpendicular to the ecliptic, not to the plane of its orbit about the earth. *N* and *S* are the north and south poles of the moon. When the moon is in position *A* a man on the earth can see several degrees beyond the moon's north pole. When it is in position *B*, a half-month later, he can see approximately the same distance beyond the south pole.

basis of whether or not *external* impact was a factor in their origin. There is need for some single term to encompass loosely all craterlike formations that may be considered, in some context, as being non-impact. The name endocrater is suggested for this heterogeneous aggregation. Ectocrater could be used for all others, but the single adjective *impact* is widely used and can suffice.

Considerable difficulty in the identification of lunar features arises from the fact that the moon does not quite keep exactly the same face toward us. Certain features near the limb, or apparent edge, sometimes disappear "around the corner" as a result of this irregularity or tipping, and even when they are visible foreshortening can distort them very much. This tipping is known as *libration,* because of the resemblance of its back-and-forth motion to the up-and-down motion of a balance scale (libra is the Latin word for such a scale). The librations are responsible for irregularities of about 16° in the face which the moon turns toward the earth. There are four kinds of libration, two of which have a significant effect on the movements and appearance of the moon.

The first of these is *libration in longitude.* Despite the fact that the moon never can have had any real oceans, the earth has produced tides on its surface. These tides have exerted a frictional drag on the moon, slowing its rotation just as the lunar tides are slowing the rotation of the earth today. The tidal effect of the earth on its relatively small satellite is so great that the moon's rotation has been slowed till it equals the period of its revolution about the earth and the moon is forced to keep one face toward the earth all the time. If its orbit around the earth were circular, the moon would circle the earth at a constant speed, completing each orbital revolution in constant phase with its rotation about its axis. But, the orbit is quite oval in shape. At the point where the orbit comes closest to the earth, the force of gravitation causes the moon to increase its speed. A half-month later, when it is farthest from the earth, the lessened force of the earth's gravity has caused the moon to slow down. During this time of decreased orbital speed the moon continues to rotate about its axis at a constant speed, and we, therefore, see somewhat more of its surface at one edge than we would have if both speeds had continued constant. During the time of increased orbital speed, the rotation of the moon falls behind, as it were, and we can see the same extra amount of its surface at the other

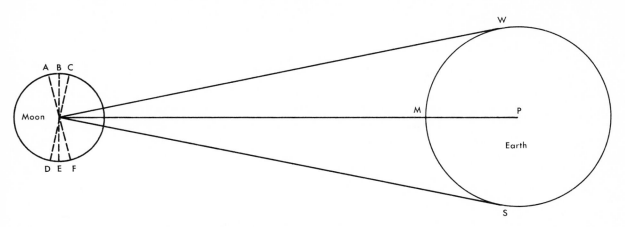

Figure 8. Diurnal libration. In this diagram the observer is looking down from a position above the earth's north pole. He sees the earth turning counterclockwise about its pole in a day and the moon revolving in the same direction about the earth in a month. When the daily spinning of the earth carries a person to the point W, the moon rises for him. When it has taken him to M the moon is on his meridian and when he reaches S the moon is setting. When the moon is rising he can see all the way around to A, but at the opposite limb cannot see beyond F. When the moon is on his meridian his vision is limited to B and E. When the moon is setting the boundaries of the half visible to him are C and D. In other words, he can see alternately a degree beyond the mean position of each limb.

limb. As a result of all this, at one time we can see nearly eight degrees "around" the eastern limb, and a half-month later an equal distance at the western limb instead becomes visible. Large librations of opposite sign on Plates 4–3 and 4–9 change the position of Mare Symthii from nearside to farside.

The second important libration is the *libration in latitude*, which results from a similar tipping in the north and south direction. The plane of the moon's equator of rotation is not in the plane of its orbit around the earth but makes an angle of a little less than seven degrees with it. As a result, at one time of the month we can see about seven degrees past the north pole and a half-month later seven degrees past the south pole. On Plate 4–3 the moon is tipped by almost the maximum amount to the south. On Plates 4–9 and 5–2 it is tipped as much to the north.

Diurnal libration is rather small and is due only to the diameter of the earth. The accompanying diagram, which of course is not drawn to scale, may assist in understanding it. The diameter of the moon, as seen from the earth, is half a degree, while that of the earth, as seen from the moon, is two degrees. The average distance between their centers is thirty times the

diameter of the earth. As a result, the moon seems to tip slightly between its rising and setting.

Finally, the pole of the moon's rotation is not quite 90° from the plane in which it and the earth move about the sun, missing by about 1½ degrees. This produces a fourth tiny libration, which is of interest only to certain astronomical specialists.

The longitude and latitude of lunar features are measured in the same manner as for terrestrial features. The coordinate origin, or reference point, is the point that would be the center of the moon's visible disk if all librations were simultaneously at their zero values. (On the earth the comparable reference point is the intersection of the Greenwich meridian with the terrestrial equator.) Longitude is measured 360° around the equator from this point. That is, an observer standing on the moon and facing south will have increasing longitude toward his left. Still another way of saying it is that for an observer at the north pole, longitude increases counterclockwise. As on the earth, latitude is measured along meridians and reaches 90° at the poles. We call these coordinates selenographic longitude and latitude.

The librations cause this reference point to

oscillate irregularly around the center of the actual visible disk. As a result the height of the sun above the horizon for any point on the moon's surface is different this month from what it will be at exactly the same phase next month. For example, the sun will not rise on Copernicus at quite the same phase in successive months. The difference is great enough to bother any systematic observer. *The American Ephemeris* ° tabulates for the beginning of each day of the year a quantity called the "colongitude of the sun." This quantity is equal to the negative of the longitude of any feature on the moon's equator for which the sun is rising at the instant. It gives a good approximation to the time of sunrise for a wide belt on each side of the equator. It is tabulated for each feature of the list at the end of this chapter, except for those which are too close to the poles for it to have much value. A more complete explanation is in the appendix on page 183–184.

This chapter includes, as Plates 3–1 and 3–2, a very comprehensive, photographic map of the moon. It is composed of two half moon photographs from the famous series made by J. H. Moore and J. F. Chappell, using the 36-inch refractor of the Lick Observatory at Mount Hamilton. Their procedure is described on page 181. (A slight difference in the librations causes only minor difficulty in use of the two chosen pictures as a map, and that little is found only in high latitudes.)

These photographs have been superposed on an arbitrary grid with x and y coordinate numbers running to the right and upward from the lower left corner. This coordinate system has no negative numbers and is convenient for identifying features. (For almost any other study of the lunar system the scale adopted by the International Astronomical Union in 1932 should be used.) As is almost universally the practice today among astronomers, south is mounted at the top and the direction which has habitually been called east at the right hand side. This causes the reader to see the moon on his map in the

same orientation as he sees it in an astronomical telescope. The astronomical convention has been to define east on the moon as toward the limb that we see to the east in our own sky. This arbitrary convention was convenient for the early astronomers but it has caused the sun to rise in the west on the moon despite the fact that the moon rotates on its axis in the same direction that the earth does. Until this decade that has been unimportant.

The International Astronomical Union adopted at its triennial meeting in August 1961 the following resolution:

"*Resolution Number 1*

"For compiling new maps of the Moon, the following conventions are recommended:

"Astronomical maps for purposes of telescopic observations are oriented according to the astronomical practice, the South being up. To remove confusion the terms East and West are deleted.

"Astronomical maps for direct exploration purposes, are printed in agreement with ordinary terrestrial mapping, North being up, East at right and West at left.

"Altitudes and distances are given in the Metric System."

East and west on the topographical maps are the exact opposite of the older astronomical books. Almost every book to date has followed the former custom. In this text, a man standing on the moon and facing south will have sunrise on his left and sunset on his right. For the next few years the changing convention will be troublesome but under twentieth-century space plans it is necessary.

An alphabetic index of 243 features of the moon will be found at the end of this chapter. The x and y coordinates are given, and also the longitude, in order that the user may have no difficulty in determining the approximate times of sunrise, except for features far from the equator. With the exception of Lyot and a few descriptive names enclosed in quotation marks, all the names are from the list approved by the International Astronomical Union at its 1932 and later sessions and used in the I.A.U. catalogue and maps under the title of "Named Lunar Formations." There have been inconsistencies in the past, especially in the spelling of Latinized

° *The American Ephemeris and Nautical Almanac* which can be consulted in any good library or may be purchased each year from the U.S. Superintendent of Documents, Washington, D.C. The beginning of the day is the instant when Greenwich Mean Time, now called Universal Time, is 00^h 00^m 00^s.

names. The official spellings are used here even in those cases where a different one might be preferable. It is better to have worldwide acceptance than to attempt to improve certain usages.*

There is a very easy way to use this map to identify any feature named in the index. Lay a piece of heavy bond paper along the x scale at the top of the map and carefully mark on it the grid coordinates printed there. To identify a feature seen on the map, lay the paper scale horizontally across the center of the object and read the x coordinate from the scale where it crosses the feature and the y coordinate from the scales at the sides of the map and then look for those coordinates in the index. To find an object for which the coordinates are given, place the scale horizontally at the given y value and then look for the object where the scale shows the given x coordinate.

For large objects such as the maria and some of the mountain-walled plains, the listed coordinates apply to a point near the center of the object. Care has been exercised to avoid designating large features by coordinates that are close to some prominent smaller object within the feature. Otherwise a beginner who did not know, for example, whether Mare Imbrium is large or small might become confused.

A photographic map is at a disadvantage in showing features that lie so close to the limb that they become unobservable when the librations are unfavorable, but are rather easy to observe when the librations are favorable. No ordinary type of map could possibly show such a feature (the walled plain Bailly is an example) under both these conditions; a globe would be required. In such cases a drawn map may have an advantage over the photographic kind. Usually it is made for the mean libration position, and it can even be distorted slightly to show a bit of what lies around the limb. But drawn maps have shortcomings. First, almost all of them are inaccurate in detail. Moreover, the fact that most of the features are drawn merely as lines, without any of the subtle differences in shading, is disadvantageous.

* At its 1961 meeting the I.A.U. made a number of changes in spellings and designations which were not yet available when the manuscript for this book received its final revisions.

The nearest approach to a perfect map (other than a globe) would require hundreds of pages of photographic prints. It would be produced for a dozen colongitudes and various combinations of librations. Some two dozen sheets would be required to cover the lunar surface for each situation; the pages would be very large and there would be a total of some 1,000 photographic prints. Except for use in the most specialized lunar research, the advantages would not be worth the cost and the bulk. A practical approximation of such an ideal map is the large lunar atlas made by Dr. Gerard P. Kuiper and published in 1960 by the University of Chicago. The supplementary atlas made by D. W. G. Arthur and E. A. Whitaker from some of Kuiper's sheets is the most useful yet prepared for the student whose research requires accurate quantitative data.

The almost 250 features listed below are not necessarily the most important ones. There would be considerable disagreement with respect to any such selection, and any individual would probably change his own choices from year to year. Primarily the listed features are the ones that are mentioned in this book, with some additional objects included, particularly in thinly identified areas. The International Astronomical Union has made nearly 700 lunar feature designations official, with several thousand additional sub-designations.

To prepare a detailed map which will be convenient and yet will satisfy most of the requirements of both the amateur and the professional astronomer, the moon has been divided into 30 overlapping sections. The four "corner" ones have been mounted as one—Plate 3–3. The other 26 comprise the large photographs, Plates 3–4 to 3–29. Each of the features included in the following list has been labeled on one or more of these maps. For the largest features, the name tab is either repeated in various locations or is placed near the center of the object, for example, Oceanus Procellarum on Plates 3–21, 3–24, and 3–27. To make these sections, the Lick Observatory pictures mounted on the grid as Plates 3–1 and 3–2 were much enlarged and then cut. Use of the same two plates for the coordinate maps and the enlarged sections makes identification very easy.

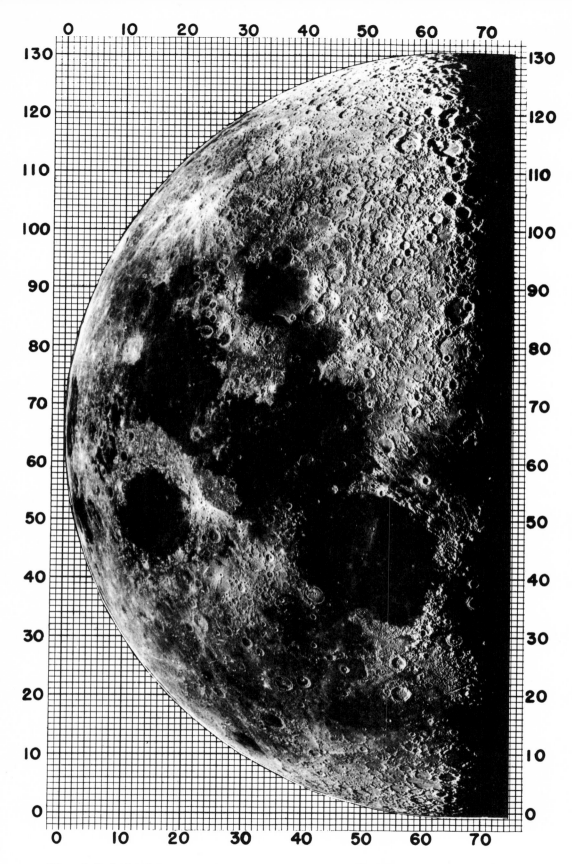

Plate 3–1. Lick Observatory, 1938 May 7^d 04^h 47^m UT, phase 6.97 days, colongitude 0°. This and Plate 3–2 form a general map. See pages 20–21 for explanation of grid and Table 4 for the grid coordinates and the colongitudes of the sun at time of sunrise for 243 lunar features. Plates 3–4 to 3–16 and part of Plate 3–3 are enlarged, overlapping sections of this plate.

Plate 3–2. Lick Observatory, 1937 October 26ᵈ 13ʰ 41ᵐ UT, phase 22.07 days, colongitude 174°. Plates 3–17 to 3–29 are enlarged sections of this plate.

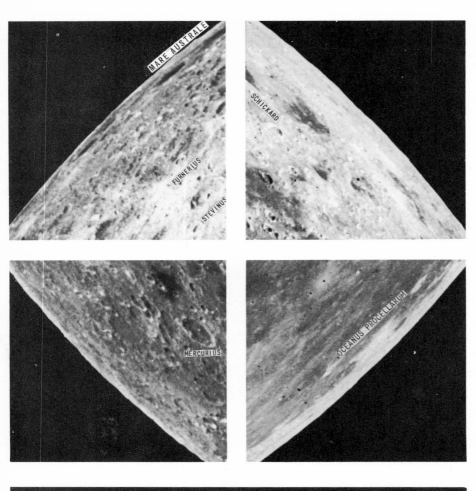

Plate 3–3. Left to right: upper left, upper right, lower left, and lower right sections of Plates 3–1 and 3–2.

Plate 3–4. Notable in this section are the Furnerius-Stevinus ray system, the Rheita depression, Mare Australe, Janssen, and long scarps which have been partly destroyed by more recent activity. See Plate 3–1 for technical details.

Plate 3–5. In the southern (top) part of this picture is a vast, mostly right and left depression which extends almost across the section. The boundaries are so low, and it has been so nearly destroyed by later changes that it is observable only under a low sun. See Plate 3–1 for technical details.

Plate 3–6. Mare Foecunditatis with Stevinus, Petavius, Vendelinus, and Langrenus in line. Lower right Messier and W. H. Pickering with the famous double ray. See Plate 3–1 for technical details.

Plate 3–7. Theophilus with Mare Nectaris and Fracastorius. The Altai Scarp is at the upper right. A great scarp runs southward from Gutenberg to the left-hand shore of Nectaris. See Plate 3–1 for technical details.

Plate 3–8. Area to the right of the Altai Scarp. Notice the very long irregular scarp southward from Albategnius to southern edge of the section. It is the right boundary of a depression which is bounded on the left by an arc of six great ringed plains. See Plate 3–1 for technical details.

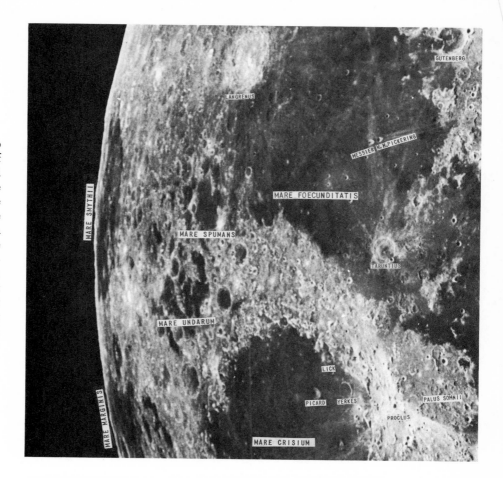

Plate 3–9. The great group of "Western Maria." All of these maria can be observed at the right-hand limb of the Russian photograph of the farside of the moon (Plate 18–1). Notice how Maria Spumans and Undarum are composed mostly of not entirely merged small sunken areas. Mare Smythii is almost the size of Mare Crisium but suffers from extreme right-left foreshortening. See Plate 3–1 for technical details.

Plate 3–10. The section consists, primarily, of Mare Tranquillitatis. See Plate 3–1 for technical details.

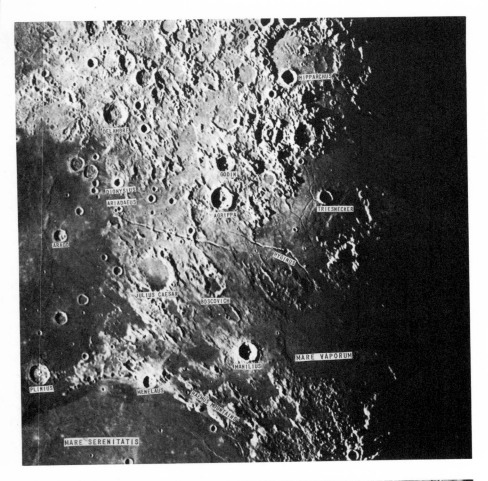

Plate 3–11. This shows the greatest of rill systems, the triple system of Triesnecker, at the terminator, Hyginus, and Ariadaeus. At the upper edge is Hipparchus, a very old, almost obliterated walled plain. Note the "finger" of smoother surface down and left from it to the Ariadaeus rill. See Plate 3–1 for technical details.

Plate 3–12. Note the "ghosts" on the northern floor of Mare Crisium. Note that there are no rays to the upper right from Proclus through Palus Somnii. The libration is unusually favorable to Mare Marginis. See Plate 3–1 for technical details.

Plate 3–13. Proclus is in the upper left. Posidonius is on the left hand of Mare Serenitatis. See Plate 3–1 for technical details.

Plate 3–14. Mare Serenitatis and the strait which connects it to Mare Imbrium. Notice the great ridge in the left of Serenitatis. Linné is on the right part of the floor. Aristillus and Autolycus are on the terminator. See Plate 3–1 for technical details.

Plate 3–15. Notice Atlas and Hercules. The variable black spot on the floor of Atlas makes it a favorite of observers. See Plate 3–1 for technical details.

Plate 3–16. The Alpine Valley is at the terminator. Aristoteles and Eudoxus are above the central part of the section. Mare Frigoris crosses the center just below Aristoteles. See Plate 3–1 for technical details.

Plate 3–17. Clavius to Deslandres. Notice that Clavius (the second largest of all walled plains) lies in the right part of a still older but much larger depression, now barely observable and only seen at all when near the terminator. Tycho is rather inconspicuous under a low sun. See Plate 3–2 for technical details.

Plate 3–18. Area right of Clavius and Tycho. This section contains the much elongated walled plain, Schiller. Near the limb is the tremendous walled plain Schickard, actually a small mare. Just above it is strange Wargentin. Unfortunately librations hid Bailly, which was just beyond the limb when the picture was made. It is larger than Clavius and should be classed as a mare. See Plate 3–2 for technical details.

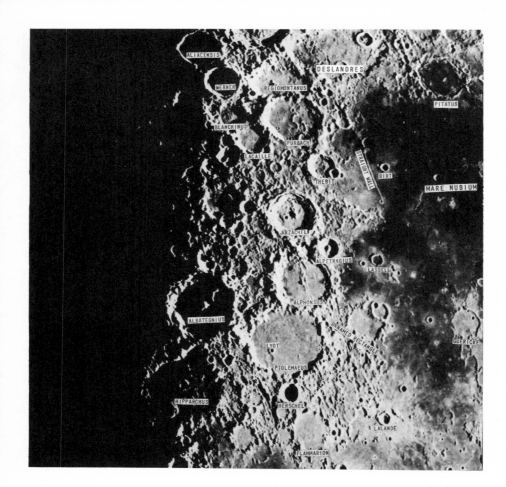

Plate 3–19. Hipparchus, Albategnius, Ptolemaeus, Alphonsus, Arzachel, Pitatus, Straight Wall, and Mare Nubium. See Plate 3–2 for technical details.

Plate 3–20. The Maria Nubium and Humorum. Note the great double ray from Tycho crossing Nubium. Note Gassendi at northern shore of Humorum. "Ghosts" are conspicuous on the floor of Nubium, which received its name from them. See Plate 3–2 for technical details.

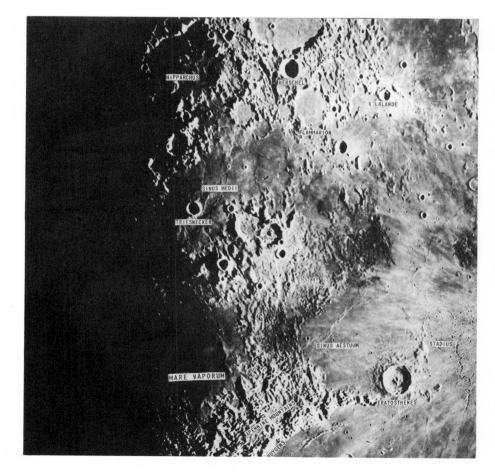

Plate 3–21. The extremely bright ringed plain Byrgius is right of Mare Humorum and near the limb. Notice the great "ghost" Letronne directly north of Gassendi. See Plate 3–2 for technical details.

Plate 3–22. Central part of the lunar disk. Note the rough area north of Sinus Medii. It is almost a large island but is connected by an isthmus to the Apennines. Note the two rough black areas on its right. They are almost unique. The Apennines have many small craters on them. See Plate 3–2 for technical details.

Plate 3–23. The Copernicus area. This region is the subject of Chapter 7. The ray system is one of the greatest features of the moon. See Plate 3–2 for technical details.

Plate 3–24. Kepler and its ray system, right to the limb. Near the limb is Grimaldi, which should be classed as a small sea. See Plate 3–2 for technical details.

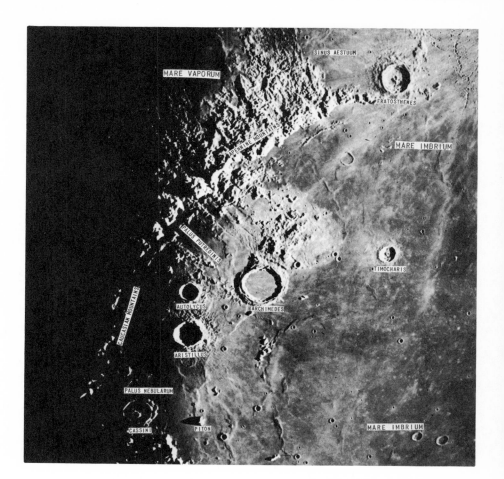

Plate 3–25. Apennines and northward along the left-hand part of Mare Imbrium. Note Archimedes and its rill system, the narrow radial valleys leading from Aristillus, and the ridges in western Imbrium. See Plate 3–2 for technical details.

Plate 3–26. Mare Imbrium. Note the complex structure of rays from Copernicus. See Plate 3–2 for technical details.

Plate 3–27. Aristarchus and its ray system, interconnecting with systems of Copernicus, Kepler, Olbers (at extreme right), and Seleucus. Aristarchus is brightest feature on the moon. Herodotus is just right of it. Schroeter's Valley is north of the two. Note the disturbed ground to their north. See Plate 3–2 for technical details.

Plate 3–28. Plato with Mare Imbrium to the south and Mare Frigoris to the north. Note the ridges in the left part of Imbrium. See Plate 3–2 for technical details.

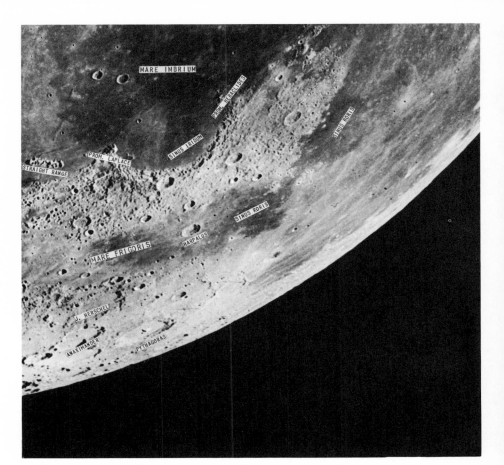

Plate 3–29. At Sinus Iridum (the Bay of Rainbows). This is the remnant of a large walled plain. The partial destruction was similar to that at the Straight Wall. The right end of Mare Frigoris is just below it. See Plate 3–2 for technical details.

Table 4

Name of feature	x	y	Selenographic colongitude at sunrise	Name of feature	x	y	Selenographic colongitude at sunrise
Abenezra	57	96	349°	Aristoteles	56	20	343°
Abulfeda	56	88	346	Arzachel	73	92	3
Agrippa	58	69	350	Atlas	57	22	316
Albategnius	66	84	356	Autolycus	69	38	358
Aliacensis	65	105	355	Azophi	56	97	348
Almanon	55	91	345	Bailly	85	126	65
Alphonsus	74	87	4	Ball	77	109	9
Alpine Valley	67	21	357	Barrow	64	6	355
Alps, mountains	67	20	0	Beaumont	39	92	352
Altai Scarp	47	98	340	Bessarion	107	54	37
Anaxagoras	71	6	11	Bessel	52	48	342
Anaximander	87	8	40	Biot	21	95	310
Anaximines	79	4	40	Birt	79	96	9
Apennine Mountains	72	50	5	Blancanus	77	126	21
Apianus	61	101	352	Blanchinus	67	99	358
Arago	47	66	358	Bond, W. C.	66	10	357
Archimedes	75	39	4	Bonpland	89	81	17
Ariadaeus	50	66	342	Boscovich	58	62	349
Aristarchus	112	43	47	Brayley	106	47	37
Aristillus	69	34	359	Bullialdus	92	94	22

Name of feature	x	y	Selenographic colongitude at sunrise	Name of feature	x	y	Selenographic colongitude at sunrise
Bürg	47	24	332°	Hercules	40	22	322°
Byrgius	118	94	65	Herodotus	113	43	49
Carpathian Mountains	95	55	20	Herschel	73	78	3
Carpenter	84	6	46	Herschel, Caroline	97	33	31
Cassini	65	25	356	Herschel, John	86	10	40
"Cassini's Bright Spot"	73	106	4	Hesiodus	85	103	16
Catharina	45	92	337	Hind	62	82	352
Caucasian Mountains	62	32	350	Hind C	61	82	351
Censorinus	35	73	328	Hippalus	98	97	30
Clavius	75	124	15	Hipparchus	65	78	354
Cleomedes	20	40	304	Hommel	50	121	326
Conon	68	49	358	Hortensius	100	64	28
Copernicus	93	60	20	Huggins	70	113	3
Cordilleras, mountains	121	93		Huygens, Mount	73	49	4
Curtius	64	127	356	Hyginus	64	65	354
Cuvier	61	121	351	Jansen	40	56	351
Cyrillus	44	87	335	Janssen	38	114	320
D'Alembert Mountains	127	76	90	Julius Caesar	54	63	345
Delambre	51	75	342	Kepler	108	61	38
De La Rue	41	12	310	Kepler A	107	62	36
Deslandres	74	106	5	Lacaille	69	97	358
Dionysius	51	70	343	Lahire	94	40	25
Doerfel Mountains	89	125		Lalande	80	77	9
Doppelmayer	106	101	41	Lambert	91	42	21
Endymion	35	15	306	Landsberg	99	71	26
Eratosthenes	83	55	12	Langrenus	11	79	300
Euclides	101	80	29	Laplace, Prom.	88	22	26
Eudoxus	56	25	344	Lassell	79	88	8
Euler	98	45	28	Lee	104	103	40
Fabricius	35	113	319	Leibnitz Mountains	55	130	
Flammarion	75	75	4	Le Monnier	39	42	330
Flamsteed	113	75	44	Letronne	112	83	42
Fracastorius	36	95	327	Lexell	73	108	5
Fra Mauro	90	79	17	Licetus	63	119	354
Furnerius	20	105	300	Lick	18	56	308
Gärtner	49	13	326	Lilius	64	123	354
Gassendi	108	90	40	Linné	58	42	348
Geber	55	94	346	Longomontanus	84	118	22
Geminus	22	35	304	Lyot	72	81	1
Godin	58	71	350	Macrobius	25	47	314
Goldschmidt	67	5	3	Mädler	38	85	330
Gould	88	92	17	Maginus	72	119	7
Grimaldi	126	74	67	Manilius	60	57	351
Gruemberger	70	127	12	Mare Australe	25	115	275
Guericke	86	84	14	Mare Crisium	15	50	300
Gutenberg	26	81	318	Mare Foecunditatis	18	75	305
Hadley, Mount	65	41	355	Mare Frigoris	45–100	14	
Haemus Mountains	60	50	345	Mare Humboldtianum	31	12	285
Harpalus	94	16	44	Mare Humorum	105	96	30
Hell	77	105	8	Mare Imbrium	90	35	20
Heraclides, Prom.	96	26	35	Mare Marginis	3	50	280

Name of feature	x	y	Selenographic colongitude at sunrise	Name of feature	x	y	Selenographic colongitude at sunrise
Mare Nectaris	35	90	330°	Pytheas	91	48	21°
Mare Nubium	83	94	15	Rabbi Levi	48	109	336
Mare Serenitatis	52	42	340	Ramsden	97	105	31
Mare Smythii	1	68	280	Regiomontanus	71	102	2
Mare Spumans	8	67	295	Reiner	116	65	55
Mare Tranquillitatis	40	62	330	Reinhold	95	68	23
Mare Undarum	8	61	292	Rheita	30	109	314
Mare Vaporum	65	58	355	Rheita Valley	31	112	314
Marius	114	56	50	Riccioli	127	70	75
Maurolycus	57	115	345	Rook Mountains	110	108	90
Menelaus	53	55	344	Rosenberger	47	122	318
Mercurius	26	21	295	Rosse	34	92	326
Mersenius	113	93	48	Rutherford	72	125	13
Messala	23	32	302	Scheiner	80	124	27
Messier	21	73	313	Schickard	104	113	55
Metius	33	112	317	Schiller	93	119	39
Meton	61	5	338	Schroeter's Valley	113	42	49
Milichius	102	60	30	Seleucus	122	44	66
Miller	68	111	0	Sinus Aestuum	80	58	10
Moretus	67	128	7	Sinus Iridum	93	22	32
Nasireddin	68	113	1	"Sinus Iridum Highlands"	90	20	35
Newton	70	130	18	Sinus Medii	72	70	0
Oceanus Procellarum	120	35–85	45	Sinus Roris	104	23	50
Olbers	127	59	76	Snellius	21	101	304
Opelt	88	90	17	Stadius	86	60	13
Orontius	72	112	4	Stevinus	23	104	306
"Oval Rays"	86	64	14	Stöfler	62	115	354
Palus Nebularum	70	31	0	Strabo	42	10	307
Palus Putredinis	70	42	0	Straight Range	83	21	21
Palus Somnii	25	54	318	Straight Wall	78	96	8
Parry	88	80	16	Taruntius	22	64	314
Petavius	16	96	300	Taurus Mountains	30	35	320
Philolaus	77	5	30	Teneriffe Range	79	21	15
Phocylides	98	119	56	Thales	44	10	310
Picard	17	54	306	Thebit	75	90	5
Piccolomini	39	103	328	Theophilus	42	85	333
Pickering, W. H.	22	73	314	Timocharis	84	42	13
Pico, Mount	76	23	9	Tobias Mayer	99	53	29
Pitatus	83	103	13	Triesnecker	66	69	356
Pitiscus	49	117	330	Tycho	78	114	12
Piton, Mount	71	28	2	Vendelinus	12	87	300
Plato	76	18	9	Vitello	102	102	37
Playfair	61	99	302	Vlacq	48	120	323
Plinius	45	55	336	Walter	70	106	359
Polybius	43	97	335	Wargentin	103	115	60
Posidonius	42	36	331	Werner	67	102	357
Proclus	23	52	314	Wichmann	108	79	37
Ptolemaeus	74	82	3	Wilhelm I	85	114	20
Purbach	72	99	3	Wrottesley	18	96	304
Pyrenees Mountains	28	87	320	Yerkes	21	53	310
Pythagoras	90	8	60	Zach	64	125	355

4 THE WAXING MOON

Almost everyone is awed by his first look at the moon through a telescope. Observing it is fascinating for a while. But interest palls soon unless one begins to study special features in sufficient detail to become quite familiar with them. This chapter and the two that follow consider the moon as a whole. They contain only brief descriptions of some of the most important features. Detailed accounts of most of the objects mentioned here and of certain others, with explanations of their possible origins, are given in later chapters and illustrated by numerous enlarged photographs. It is hoped that these three general survey chapters will induce some of the thousands who own adequate telescopes to use their instruments systematically and to learn at first hand of some of the wonders that are visible. For the more casual reader photographs will suffice quite well.

When the thin crescent moon can first be observed it appears as on Plate 4–1. The photograph exhibits the moon at phase 2.66 days— that is, 2.66 days after it was most closely in the direct earth-sun line. At this phase the moon is still so nearly in line with the sun that by the time the sky is dark enough for a photograph to be made the moon is very low in the west. The

mountings of most of the great telescopes will not permit observations so close to the horizon. Moreover, at low altitudes the atmosphere is usually too unsteady to permit crisp photographic images. The amateur, visual observer will also have difficulty with his portable telescope at this phase, for the air is "boiling" too much in his field of view to allow him to see fine detail. On the March evening when this photograph was made, conditions were unusually good. It should be noted that the sunrise terminator has barely reached the left shore of Mare Crisium.

By the next evening (Plate 4–2) a very different landscape may be observed. Not only has the terminator moved far into areas entirely dark the night before, but some of the features appear to be entirely different in form from what they were on the first evening. During the month the observer will discover that an interval of only a few days causes the appearance of such craters as Furnerius, Tycho, and Copernicus to change so much that they are no longer recognizable. The changes caused by differences in length and direction of shadows also can hardly be believed until they are experienced. But if the directions given in Chapter 3 are followed, there should be little difficulty in identifying most objects. On

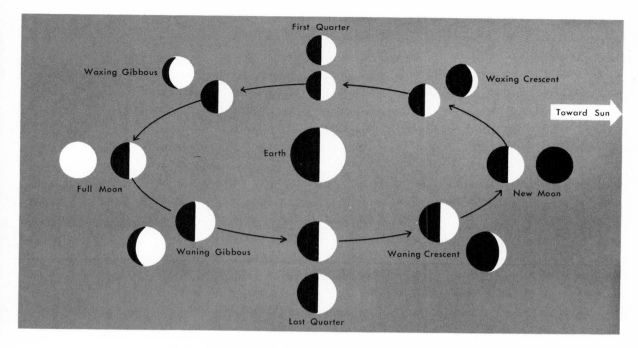

Figure 9. Phases of the moon. As the moon travels around the earth, one-half is in sunlight and one-half in darkness. However, varying amounts of the sunlit hemisphere are turned toward the earth, creating the phases seen from earth (outer figures).

all of these views the usual astronomical convention of placing north at the bottom is followed. The sun rises on each equatorial object when the colongitude at the moment equals the negative of its longitude. See table 4 in Chapter 3. The rule holds quite well throughout a wide belt on each side of the equator.

During the phases of four to six days the moon displays a wide variety of features for examination in its early morning sunshine. One very conspicuous example is Mare Crisium, the Sea of Crises. During this interval, as shown by Plates 4–2—4–7, its floor exhibits much lacy detail. Part of this, especially in the northern portion, is composed of "ghosts"—craters that ap-

parently predated the mare and sank with the surrounding area during its formation. It seems probable that they were almost completely engulfed by the sea of molten rock, but not quite completely enough to obliterate all traces of their existence. When the sun is practically at the horizon it is actually possible to observe short shadows from a couple of the sunken walls. The most conspicuous of the ghosts still rise very slightly above the surface of the "sea." If the maria had been the results, primarily, of great explosions 'we would not expect to find these traces from the past.

The observer should also look (Plates 4–2 and 10–9) for the "continental shelf" that surrounds

Figure 10. Combined earth and moon orbits. Both the earth and the moon revolve about the sun, but at the same time the moon revolves about the earth, creating the intertwined trace shown here.

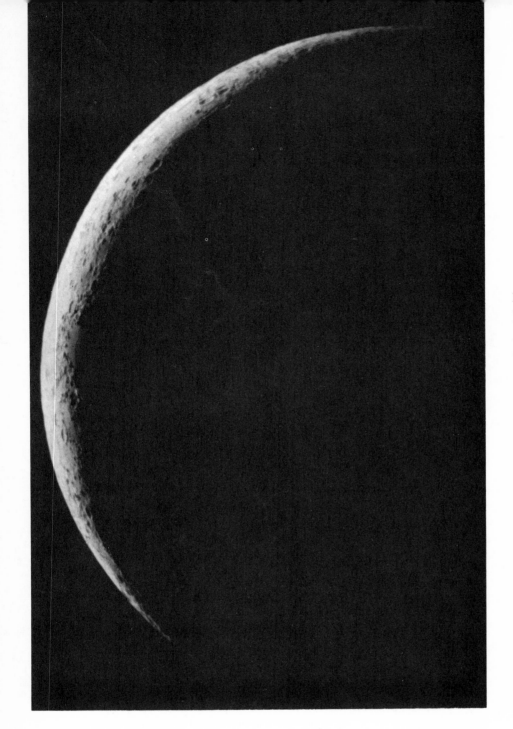

Plate 4–1. Griffith Observatory, 1959 March 12^d 02^h 38^m UT, phase 2.66 days, colongitude 298°. Paul E. Roques with 12-inch Zeiss refractor, Kodak Royal Pan Film, C. G. 3385 filter (yellow). Principally the left shore of Mare Foecunditatis.

the central part of Mare Crisium. It produces a sudden deepening of the floor, exactly as do the continental shelves of our terrestrial oceans. Ridges are common on mare floors but the boundary of this central area is not a ridge. Under a low morning sun the left hand boundary is darker than the neighboring floor, while the

right hand boundary is lighter. This is reversed during the time before sunset. The boundary is a true scarp, and it provides strong evidence that not all of the sinking occurred at one time, but that a final subsidence came after the rock had lost much of its fluidity.

All around the shoreline of Mare Crisium

can be seen the remains of large, old, craterlike features whose seaward walls apparently collapsed in the formation of the sea. Such remnants are common around most of the maria. In some cases they have become mere bays. In other cases their seaward walls may still be observed under proper illumination. They present part of the evidence of the process by which the maria were formed.

In the first days during which the crescent moon can be observed in the evening sky, the terminator moves to the right across Mare Foecunditatis, which is south of Mare Crisium. In Plate 4–2 it is just entering that area. On Plate 4–2 the ridges in the left hand part of that mare show nicely and the terminator has just passed the craters Messier and W. H. Pickering. Shadow effects cause the apparent sizes and shapes of

these two features to change during the month. It is one of the most common characteristics of human beings to prefer an exciting explanation of data to the prosaic one that is usually true. This is illustrated beautifully by some of the spectacular things which have been written about these two conspicuous little craters. Chapter 15 includes a series of enlarged pictures of them (Plate 15–8) and considers what actually takes place between sunrise and sunset. The double ray extending eastward from the pair should be followed carefully. Special note should be made of the fact that the southern component of the ray is a series of bright spots. The two rays end at a crater similar in size to the primary pair but less conspicuous because of its brighter background.

Sunrise on Mare Nectaris should also be ob-

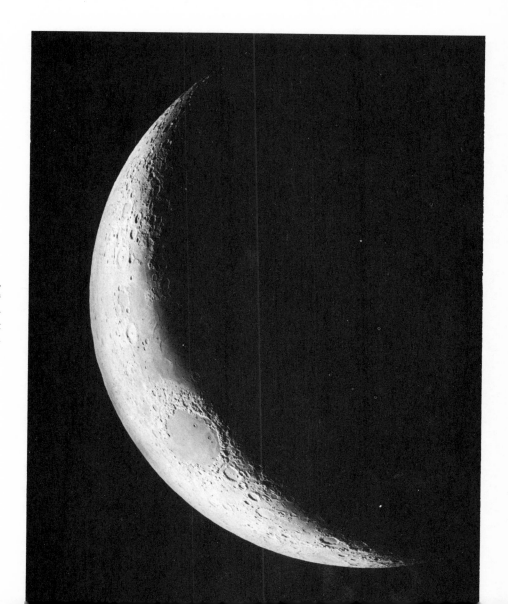

Plate 4–2. Lick Observatory, 1937 September 9^d 02^h 45^m UT, phase 4.16 days, colongitude 316°. Terminator at Rheita Valley, Mare Foecunditatis, and Proclus.

served at this time of the month. In Plate 4–3 the terminator lies across it and reveals one of the most beautiful scenes on the moon. Two scarps show exquisitely. One runs southward from Gutenberg and eventually forms part of the shoreline on the left of Nectaris. The other, nearly parallel to it, is a continental shelf within the mare. The crater Rosse can be seen on this picture almost exactly at the terminator. On Plate 4–4 the terminator is beyond Nectaris and just outlines the crest of the Altai Scarp, far to the right. This scarp is hundreds of miles long and forms an arc centered on Mare Nectaris. There is little doubt that when Nectaris was formed the sinking extended to the right and upward far beyond its shoreline.

Plate 4–5, a day later, shows the whole area beyond Nectaris and reveals that it is less rugged left of the Altai Scarp than it is farther to the right. Plate 6–3, where the arc shows dark under a setting sun, gives adequate proof that this is actually a great scarp and not a ridge, as sometimes has been thought.

Furnerius and Stevinus are visible in the upper left portion of Plate 4–2 and at this moment there is nothing to attract attention to them. On Plate 4–4 a definite brightening has occurred. But by the time the colongitude of Plate 4–5 has been reached, a craterlet on the outer right hand slope of each of them has brightened so conspicuously that the eye is caught immediately. A single day later this brightening has increased noticeably, and the great, vivid streaks of a composite ray system can be seen. From then until

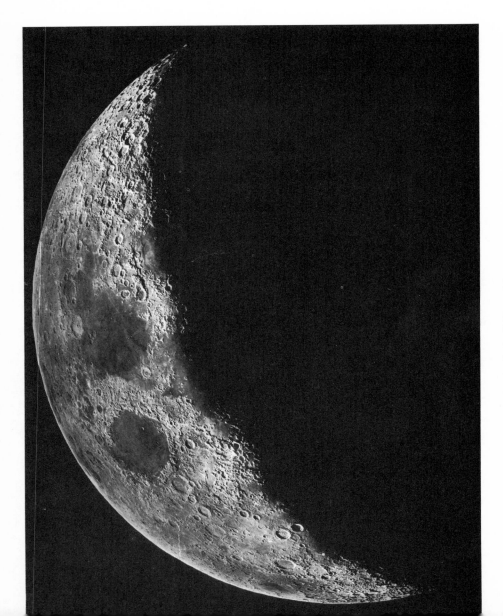

Plate 4–3. Lick Observatory, 1938 June 3ᵈ 04ʰ 02ᵐ UT, phase 4.59 days, colongitude 329°. Terminator at Janssen, at Mare Nectaris, to the right of Mare Tranquillitatis, and at Hercules.

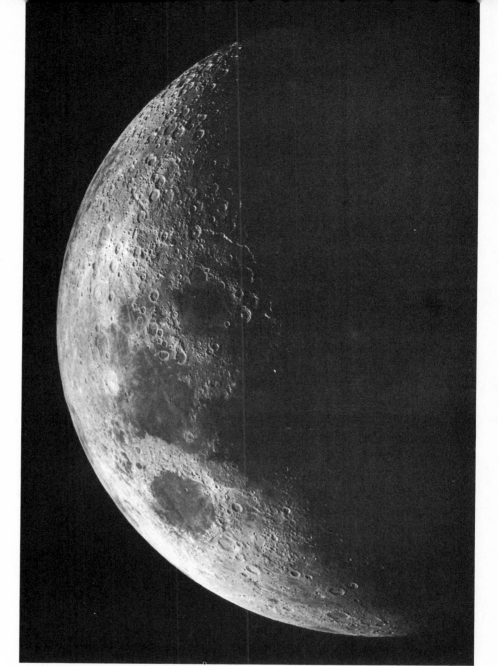

Plate 4–4. Lick Observatory, 1940 August 9^d 04^h 03^m UT, phase 5.33 days, colongitude 339°. Terminator at Altai Scarp and left shore of Mare Serenitatis.

near sunset, long after full moon, their brightness impresses even a casual observer. Shortly before full moon (Plate 4–11) this ray system can be observed to tie in with that of Tycho to form one tremendous oversystem.

Just before the half moon phase (Plate 4–5) the terminator crosses Mare Serenitatis in the northern part of the moon. This mare has a spectacular dark edging around its shoreline and is worthy of much study. A great north and south

ridge in the left hand portion of the floor is a continuation of the system that begins near Mare Nectaris and proceeds northward through Mare Tranquillitatis. The only other ridge on the moon to rival it is in Oceanus Procellarum close to the limit on the right. On Plate 4–5 the beautiful little crater Bessel is at the terminator. A day and a half later (Plate 4–7) the whole of the floor of Serenitatis is illuminated and Linné is seen as a tiny bright spot not far left of the gap con-

45

necting this mare to Mare Imbrium. Just beyond the gap are the ringed plains Aristillus and Autolycus. At this phase the great mountain ranges bounding the mare are especially conspicuous because of the long shadows they cast in late afternoon.

In the southern part of the moon one of the roughest areas of the whole surface can now be seen. The terminator enters on it near phase five days, and does not complete the passage until almost a week has passed. It is probable that this great area is characterized by some of the oldest of the extant lunar features. When the terminator (Plate 4–3) is near that gigantic "grandfather" Janssen, the shadows of its low walls are long and render it conspicuous. Each day it becomes less noticeable. During the many hundreds of millions of years (perhaps billions) since its genesis, younger features formed over it have begun to obliterate this venerable ancestor. On Plate 4–7 a still grander patriarch is conspicuous on the terminator. This monster is so shallow that it was almost completely neglected until recent years, when the geologist Spurr called attention to its unusual character. Belatedly the International Astronomical Union voted to give it the

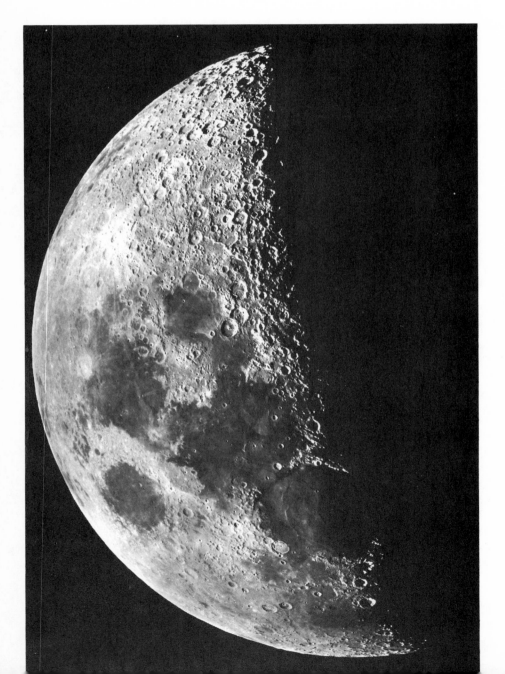

Plate 4–5. Lick Observatory, 1946 August 4^d 04^h 04^m UT, phase 6.67 days, colongitude 348°. Terminator at Maurolycus, right-hand part of Mare Serenitatis.

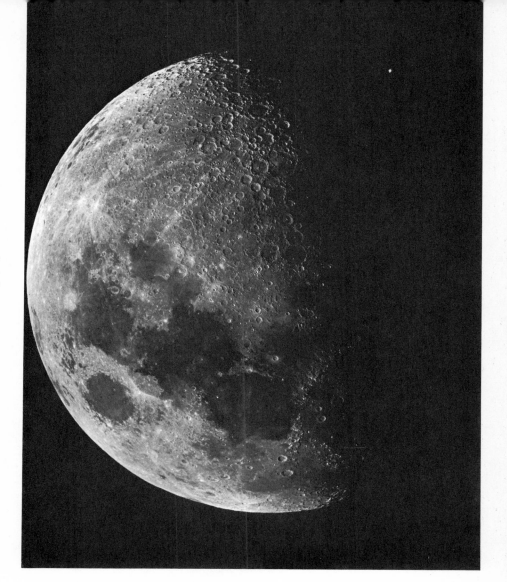

Plate 4–6. Lick Observatory, 1940 August 12^d 03^h 52^m UT, phase 8.32 days, colongitude 16°. Terminator at Clavius, Eratosthenes, and Plato.

name Deslandres. After two or three days it vanishes from sight. Then, except for the feature known as "Cassini's Bright Spot," there is nothing special to call attention to the area until the long shadows of sunset bring it into relief again at about the time of waning half moon.

The monthly changes in orientation of the lunar axis show well on Plates 4–11 and 5–2.

With Plate 4–6, at phase 8.32 days, the right part of the moon first comes under scrutiny. Clavius, a rival of Janssen, is barely hidden near the southern end of the terminator. Maginus is just to its north. Still farther north and exactly on the terminator is a smaller crater, less conspicuous than the larger ones in the southern region. Nothing about it, no matter how careful the observation, would indicate that in a very few days it will excel all other craters and rival the maria for attention. This is Tycho, possibly the seat of the most violent lunar explosion of which there is visible record. Nothing of its great ray system now appears nearby, but far to the left, where the sun already is high, its rays have begun to appear. The study of violent explosive craters and their ray systems furnishes clues to the story of lunar evolution.

The great mountain-walled plain Ptolemaeus and the craters Alphonsus and Arzachel form a chain that is seen at its best close to the terminator on Plate 4–7. As soon as the sun becomes

Plate 4–7. Lick Observatory, 1940 December 08^d 04^h 19^m UT, phase 8.80 days, colongitude 14°. Terminator at Tycho, right of Deslandres, and Eratosthenes. This plate and the preceding one illustrate an effect of the libration in longitude.

Plate 4–8. Lick Observatory, 1940 August 13^d 04^h 16^m UT, phase 9.33, colongitude 28°. Terminator right of Clavius, near Copernicus and Sinus Iridum.

Plate 4–9. Lick Observatory, 1942 July 23^d 04^h 36^m UT, phase 9.69 days, colongitude 31°. Compare Mare Crisium with Plate 4–8 for the effect of libration in longitude.

Plate 4–10. Lick Observatory, 1938 January 12^d 03^h 55^m UT, phase 10.37, colongitude 38°. Terminator at Mare Humorum, left of Kepler, and right of Sinus Iridum. Perhaps this is the best plate of the Moore-Chappell series.

high (Plate 4–11), these objects will almost disappear. At full moon phase the easiest way to recognize them will be by use of the famous tiny black spots on the floor of Alphonsus. These spots blacken more and more as the sun gets higher, or at least they assume such an aspect in comparison to the neighboring areas. It is from within Alphonsus that a very small amount of extremely low-density gas was observed to escape a few years ago. Also on this plate the terminator is almost exactly on the Straight Wall, an 80-mile-long cliff roughly a thousand feet high. That cliff

Plate 4–11. Lick Observatory, 1947 May 3^d 06^h 30^m UT, phase 12.09 days, colongitude 62°. Surface of moon beginning to take on the flatter appearance of the full moon phase. Note extreme counterclockwise orientation of the lunar meridian.

came into existence when the surface to the right of it collapsed during the formation of Mare Nubium. No other single feature on the moon, with the possible exception of the Altai Scarp, exhibits so clearly the manner of mare formation. Farther to the north the Apennines, grandest of all lunar mountain ranges and the one that most nearly resembles terrestrial ranges, are resplendent in the early morning sunshine. The scarp of these mountains, the greatest at least on this side of the moon, is seen as a boundary of Mare Imbrium. On the right hand point of the range the rising sun touches the crest of Eratosthenes. In another day or so it will look like an immense mountain that became too heavy and collapsed within itself. (The caldera of Mauna Loa in Hawaii, which formed because of the reverse drainage of lava, resembles it on a smaller scale.) Below the Apennine scarp we see the peninsula and the "marshes" that resulted from collapsed material that was not completely inundated when the formation of Mare Imbrium occurred.

In the north, close to the terminator, are the two great ringed plains Archimedes and Plato. These craters are old, and each was modified by the formation of Mare Imbrium. To the left of Plato are the Alps and the Alpine Valley, the most famous of its kind on the moon. Perhaps when the terminator is in the position of Plate 4–7, at colongitude 14°, more interesting features are strung out near it than at any other time. At this phase the left hand portion of the floor of Imbrium shows more fine detail than at any other phase until far into the waning stage shown in map on Plate 3–2. Sections of two photographs have been enlarged as Plates 10–19 and 10–20 to tell a partial story of Imbrium and its origin. No one yet knows the whole story of this largest of the maria, although some astronomers are confident that certain parts of it differ from any of the others.

Plate 4–8 for the first time reveals Copernicus, which has the advantage of standing in a rather smooth area and is therefore conspicuous from the moment sunlight first strikes its outer left hand wall. Its ray system reveals fully as long a story as does the system of Tycho. The strange oval rays to the left of Copernicus show nicely on Plate 4–10. The observer with even a moderate-sized telescope can see some of the short, elementary components of the major rays, especially in the mare area to the north. Seen with a more powerful telescope some of them display craterlets at the ends which are pointed toward Copernicus.

At this phase (Plate 4–10) the long, low ridges of Mare Imbrium are observable near the terminator, in the right hand portion of the sea, provided one uses a rather large telescope with fairly high magnifying power and on a night when seeing conditions are quite steady. Some of these ridges are more than a hundred miles long, but they may not be more than fifty feet high, so they disappear as soon as the sun is well above the horizon. At the same time the observer should look for craterlets on the part of the floor where the sun has barely risen. Some of them appear to be rounded, suggesting an origin in the collapse of such domes as may be seen in some of the smooth lunar areas.

The sun rises on Sinus Iridum, the Bay of Rainbows, between the colongitudes of Plates 4–9 and 4–10. This scene will well reward long observation. Study of the craterlets on the highlands just to the north is important in **any** consideration of origins.

In Plate 4–11, about two days before full moon, Mare Humorum has just emerged into the sunlight on the southern part of the moon. Its shoreline is especially rich in "half-craters." On its northern shore great Gassendi exhibits a lowered seawall that is actually broken at one spot. Much farther north Aristarchus, the brightest of all craters, is on the terminator. The sunlight is just beginning to cross Oceanus Procellarum, which is far larger than Mare Imbrium. It too would be called a mare if its vast size did not so greatly exceed the total area of the maria. The area south of Aristarchus and to the right of Kepler has come into good observational illumination. Much of it, especially in the general neighborhood of Marius, is unusually rich in domes and ridges and such areas should be studied carefully whenever the terminator is near them.

At this point the moon has begun to take on the appearance that is generally characteristic of full moon phase, a period that may be considered as extending from two days before until two days after the actual full moon. The next chapter deals with this four-day interval.

53

5 THE FULL MOON

At full phase the moon is more beautiful to the naked eye than at any other time. One reason may be that at the moment of its rising in the evening it appears far larger than when it is riding high above the horizon. Actually, its angular diameter at this time of its greatest apparent magnitude is smaller than it is at any other position, because the distance to the moon along a tangent to the earth's surface, as at rising or setting, is approximately 4,000 miles more than the distance along the center-to-center line when it is overhead. The reason for this well-known moon illusion is quite interesting and perhaps not widely understood by the non-scientific public.

The human eyes can estimate the size of an object, or its distance or displacement in space, up to a distance of about two hundred feet. Any estimates of size beyond that point are the result of familiarity with the thing which is observed. We know, for example, that the distant house is not merely a doll's house close at hand. Our mind tells us that it is far away although our vision cannot give even a rough estimate of the distance.

It follows from this that when the moon is far from the horizon, and there are no nearby objects with which to compare it, we automati-

cally and unconsciously bring it in toward the 200-foot distance, and it appears as a small object. (Indeed, few people realize how small the moon actually is in our sky; a dime held at a distance of a little more than six feet will exactly cover it.) But when the moon is rising or setting it is obviously farther away than some distant house or other large familiar object along the same line of vision, and we judge it to be by far the larger of the two. This illusion results from our training and cannot be experienced by a small child, who may instinctively reach out his hands to grasp the bright object. This difficulty in measuring distance is compounded by another factor. The inability of the eye to make estimates of distances may handicap a person who is not used to clear mountain air. Accustomed to haze between himself and comparatively nearby objects, he tends to allow for the haze in his estimates of long distances. Langley, a great nineteenth-century astronomer, related in his book *The New Astronomy* his experience while heading a solar eclipse expedition in the Sierra Nevadas. "The sky is cloudless, and the air so clear that all idea of the real distance and size of things is lost. The mountains, which rise in tremendous precipices above him, seem like moss covered rocks close at hand, on the tops of which, here and there, a white cloth has been dropped; but the 'moss' is great primeval forests, and the white cloth large isolated snow-fields, tantalizing the dweller in the burning desert with their delusive nearness."

Another very interesting phenomenon in connection with the moon's appearance is the effect of refraction, the bending of light by the earth's atmosphere. Refraction causes all objects to appear to be closer to the zenith than they actually are. At the horizon, where the line of vision passes through more of the atmosphere, the effect is rather large—fully a half-degree. For example, when the lower limb of the sun or moon is apparently exactly on the true horizon, the whole of the object is actually entirely below the horizon. As one looks even half a degree above the horizon, refraction becomes noticeably less. As a result of this lessening with altitude, the lower limb of the sun or moon actually at the horizon appears to be lifted toward the upper one, causing the object to appear distinctly oval, with its vertical diameter too small.

Full moon occurs at the instant during the month when the earth is most nearly in line between the sun and moon. In those months when the moon is closely enough in line north and south, an eclipse occurs. Usually the moon passes a little to the north or to the south of the earth's shadow.

At the instant of full moon, a man on the moon and at the center of the moon's visible disk would see the sun directly overhead, and would cast no shadow. Even if he were at the limb, where his shadow would be long, the shadow would be behind him and silhouetted from any view on earth, because the sun would be directly behind the shoulders of an observer on earth. The full moon shows us almost none of its black shadows.

All through a clear night the full moon provides enough light for ordinary vision, yet a light faint enough to soften and romanticize every object. The yellowish tinge of the light, caused primarily by the earth's atmospheric absorption, increases the effect of mystery and subtlety. In selecting a time to visit an observatory a non-astronomer usually requests a night of full moon, but the sight is usually disappointing because the great shining disk is almost devoid of the shadows that define lunar features.

To the naked eye, the full moon exhibits smoothish, dark areas, the maria, and brighter, mountainous regions. The pattern of the maria gives us the traditional "man in the moon," which is apparent at full moon because of variations in the small percentage of light reflected by different terrain. The walled plains and craters that were so striking during the waxing phase, and will be again in the waning moon, owe their visibility to shadow patterns. When the sun is low the long shadows of their walls exhibit spectacular detail, but of course at full moon they almost disappear. In contrast to these objects that hide from us at full moon, there are other craters that are the result of almost unbelievably violent explosions that modified the nature of the lunar surface rock. Such craters, and also the maria, become much more conspicuous under a high sun, when the extreme roughness of the surrounding territory has been minimized by lack of shadows. For example, Tycho brightens far more than any of its neighbors as the sun gains altitude. Long and rather bright streaks called "rays" extend from it in various directions for hundreds of miles (Plate 5–2). Only the greatest of the maria can rival its display at this time.

To a conspicuous but lesser degree the same thing happens to Copernicus, Kepler, Byrgius, Olbers, Aristarchus, Anaxagoras, and others. Even craterlets may show such rays conspicuously as, for example, the two just outside of Furnerius and Stevinus. Some craterlets brighten until at full phase they appear almost as stars against the moon.

The pattern that crisscrosses the full moon is a glorious one but the glare dazzles the eye of the observer at the telescope too much for him to perceive any real detail. With a low-power eyepiece to permit simultaneous viewing of the entire full moon, one can become lost in a mysterious, alien, shining, and dreamlike world of almost hypnotic appeal. But the serious investigator cannot devote much of his time to such reveries, and his studies force him to work usually at other phases. If, however, he has superior equipment, if he has lived with the moon for a long time, and if devising methods of observing the moon has become a kind of game for him, he eventually learns that there are some important things revealed by the full moon that do not appear at the other phases. Even use of a cardboard diaphragm to reduce the brightness of the image by stopping down the objective or the mirror of his telescope, or the insertion of a filter at the eyepiece, materially increases what may be observed. Partial elimination of glare is a first step toward visual study.

But elementary procedures of this kind do not improve the situation sufficiently to permit much valuable research today on the full moon. There is no way by which the astronomer can do much to overcome the lack of sufficient visual contrast. Fortunately there are other, non-visual methods that can provide assistance. The chief of these is the photographic plate. The observer can choose from a wide variety of plates and may expose and develop them in ways to obtain less contrast or to exaggerate contrast as much as he likes. He can choose plates and filters to produce photographs that appear at their brightest in any desired color. He can record the scene as it is transmitted by radiation of entirely different wavelengths from those that produce recognizable images on the human retina. He can choose plates so sensitive that they can preserve for his leisurely perusal a record made in a mere thousandth of a second. Whereas a visual observation is subject to the prejudices of the astronomer and leaves no record to display to a skeptic, what is clearly recorded on the negative is fact; only interpretation can be challenged. The human eye directly at the telescope has one advantage: When the photographic plate shows some tiny markings and cannot quite resolve them, the astronomer can use a visual telescope on a night when the air is steady to look at the area and observe a little more of the delicate detail than was recorded by the camera.

The application of photography is so vital to a comprehensive knowledge of the lunar surface, and especially of what it displays at full moon, that a digression outlining the functions and techniques of lunar photography may be useful at this point.

The first celestial photograph was a daguerreotype of the moon made in 1840 by Dr. J. W. Draper. It was of rather poor quality. Ten years later Dr. W. C. Bond, first director of the Harvard Observatory, made an excellent daguerreotype with the fifteen-inch refracting telescope of that observatory. Soon after these were taken, and as a result of their exhibition in Europe, Warren De la Rue of England became so much interested in celestial photography that he devoted the remainder of his life to it. In 1853 he made some exquisite lunar photographs, using the newly developed "wet plate" process and a thirteen-inch reflecting telescope.

By 1879 the "dry plate" process had been invented, with much advantage to every sort of photographic enterprise. During the 1880's the use of fluorescing dyes in plate emulsions extended the spectral range toward the red. The earlier plates had been very little affected by light of longer wavelengths than those of the green, and their color balance was therefore quite different from that of the human eye, which is most sensitive to the yellow wavelengths. By 1906, with the advent of "panchromatic" emulsions, red was finally able to contribute its full share to an exposure. Nineteen years later the use of still other dyes produced plates sensitive to "infrared" light, that is, to wavelengths too long to affect the human retina. Since that time the improvement of infrared plates has been steady, and today we have a rather wide range of such plates. Their speed has been much improved, varying degrees of contrast are available, still longer wavelengths are recorded; fineness of grain, which affects resolution, has been increased.

De la Rue had used a reflecting telescope because of an unavoidable defect inherent in the refracting type. Refraction is bending. What a prism does is to bend the shorter wavelengths of light, such as violet, more than it does longer ones like the red, and thus spreads white light into a spectrum. But when a lens exhibits a similar effect there is trouble. The first telescopes (three centuries ago) used only one piece of convex glass as an objective. Such a telescope brings violet light to a decidedly shorter focus than it does the red, thus distorting the image— when one color is brought to a sharp focus all other colors contributing to the image are out of focus. More than two hundred years ago Dollond lessened this trouble considerably by combining two pieces of glass of different density and different surface shapes so that each would tend to correct the defects of the other. Telescopes with such objectives are called *achromatic refractors*, although the correction is not perfect. But the loss of light involved in use of a multiple lens system in a large telescope would be very serious. The reflecting telescope, invented by Isaac Newton, brings all colors of light to exactly the same focus and is therefore free from this difficulty.

It is, nevertheless, possible to make excellent pictures of the moon with a refractor if a yellow filter is placed in front of the photographic plate. (Lenses of telescopes made for visual observations are so shaped that color difficulties are less in the yellow range than they are in either the blue or the red range. The filter excludes all the light except the range which it was designed to pass.) All but one of the pictures used to illustrate Chapter 4 were made in this manner with the 36-inch refractor of the Lick Observatory and a special yellow filter. Of course, the use of a filter increases the necessary length of the exposure. The reflector, on the other hand, does not require a filter, except for special effects, and is therefore faster than a refractor of the same light-gathering power and focal length. It is possible to "take" a picture of the moon in less than a thousandth of a second, although most exposures are of the order of a few tenths of a second. Many of the pictures used in this book were made using the 60-inch reflector at Mt. Wilson with infrared plates. In this study a filter which passes no visual light was used with them. This way the unsteadiness of the earth's atmosphere distorts the images formed by infrared light less than those formed by blue and violet.

When we prepare a full moon picture for public display, the dense parts of the negative, which picture the bright areas, may be chemically reduced until they compare more nearly with the parts that show the dark maria. Otherwise the bright areas may show merely a glare of white paper or the dark maria may be shown as an almost useless black. This has been done expertly for Plate 5–1, and the result is one of the finest full moon pictures possible for public lecturing and for illustration of popular articles. However, the part of a plate that has been overexposed and then reduced can never possess the full quality of a plate that has received proper exposure and development. Furthermore such tampering renders the plate subject to suspicion.

Plate 5–2 exhibits the moon near the full phase somewhat as it appears to the visual observer who has used a filter to avoid the glare, although no black and white photograph can do more than provide a rough approximation to the visual observation. For example, to the eye at the telescope even the maria are bright; their darkness is merely by contrast to the still brighter rough areas. But on the photographic negative, the density of the mare areas is normally much less than that of the mountainous regions. In order to make a photographic *positive* showing details of the mare floors, it must be printed for such a short time that the portion of the print representing the brighter areas of the moon will remain almost clear, telling us little. If longer printing is employed to show the detail of these brighter areas, the maria are "burned" black. It would require at least two prints to tell all that the negative can display. Of course two negatives exposed differently in rapid succession would be better than two prints from one negative. Such variations in length of exposure are merely the starting procedure for satisfactory observation of the full moon. It is necessary also to choose plates of different optimum contrast. To bring out details within the bright major rays of Tycho and Copernicus, for instance, it is necessary to use plates with great contrast.

In Plates 5–2 and 5–1, made under a high sun but with proper exposure and choice of plate, Copernicus shows surprising facets. Plate 10–22, showing Mare Imbrium, is almost ugly because of the white expanses of the bright areas, but it is one of the most useful plates ever made for the study of the floor of that mare. The student who looks at a few fine pictures is apt to feel that he "knows" the appearance of the moon. In reality he is like one of the nine blind men who examined the elephant: He knows a few aspects, and there are many. The observer who desires really to know the moon must continually experiment with new and tedious techniques. Often he learns after several nights of hard work that some approach for which he had high hopes is valueless. On the other hand, other new techniques—perhaps the use of polarized light—will have merit. The radiation-sensitive cells of the photometer could be usefully applied for a thousand hours or so to provide charts of the relative brightness of a hundred features under all sorts of conditions. Kozyrev has recently surprised lunar scientists by demonstrating that the spectrograph is needed. When each of these techniques has been pushed to the limit, the group of "blind men" who have used them may compare notes and as a result may learn something of the true appearance of their "elephant," the moon.

Plate 5–1. Lick Observatory, 1946 January 17^d 07^h 51^m UT, phase 13.80, colongitude 82°. This is a beautiful plate taken about two-thirds of a day before full moon. The plate has been specially printed to avoid the extreme full moon contrast. Compare with Plate 5–2 which has not been so treated.

Plate 5–2. Lick Observatory, 1939 July 31ᵈ 07ʰ 29ᵐ UT, phase 14.43, colongitude 89°. This plate was exposed about two hours before full moon. Tycho, Copernicus, and their ray systems almost give the illusion of explosions taking place when the exposure was made.

6 THE WANING MOON

The preceding chapters on the waxing and the full moon described the aspects of the moon with which amateurs are most familiar, and for an obvious reason: those are the phases that are observable in the evening sky. The waning moon is another matter, and a much less convenient one. Even one day after full moon the moon does not rise until almost an hour after sunset. One week later it rises at midnight, and at the end of the phase it withholds its appearance until dawn. The amateur who observes systematically under these conditions is of no ordinary breed.

Just before full moon, objects in the sunrise area very close to the right hand limb reveal their detailed structure best. Just after full moon much the same is true for the features close to the left hand limb, which we now see almost as plainly in the sunset as when the waxing moon was a thin crescent. Only the visual impact of the brightness of the rest of the moon interferes. On the photographic plate the images are equally good. However, the reversed direction of the shadows from the setting sun does help interpretation very much when we compare the two views.

At phase 16.3 (Plate 6–1) the chain of very large craters northward from Furnerius through Petavius, Vandelinus, and Langrenus can be seen plainly. It is almost sunset on them. Actually we can usually see this chain better after full moon than we could on the waxing crescent because the latter is observed close to our horizon, where the earth's atmosphere nearly always interferes. On the waxing crescent the inner left hand walls of the craters were dark and the right hand ones were brilliantly illuminated; now the condition is reversed. The observer who wishes to look for rills, craterlets, and other fine features has details to observe different from those he had two weeks before.

Now Mare Crisium revises the story it told during the early phase. The floor still shows the same lacy detail, the shores have the same bays, and the shape is unchanged (unless the librations have changed the foreshortening by a shift in the distance of the mare from the limb). But now the second brightest feature of the moon makes its appearance just off the right hand shore, attracting almost as much attention as the mare itself. This is the extremely bright explosive crater Proclus. Craters of this kind, which have resulted from an unusually violent explosion, brighten under a high sun much more than do the surrounding areas. (Even Tycho is not conspicuous when the sun is near the horizon.) When the sun was rising on Mare Crisium it was even lower on Proclus. Now, when the sunset terminator just touches the left hand shore of the mare, the sun still is rather far from the horizon of Proclus. Once more the observer should look at the peculiar ray system of Proclus and should compare the right hand gap of the system with the similar one in the greater system of Tycho. The rays cannot be seen to the right where apparently a partial sinking produced a "swamp" called Palus Somnii, the marsh of sleep. (Its low, rough surface is seen most clearly on Plate 6–2.) There is a sharp boundary on the right between the swamp and Mare Tranquillitatis.

At approximately this phase of 16 days (Plate 6–1) the great ray to the left from Tycho to Mare Nectaris can be studied best. It should be noted that it is actually two rays and not one, being doubled over much of its length, and that most of its brightness comes from craters along it.

Plato, in the northern area, is always interesting and at this phase the craters and partial craters around its rim can be observed to good advantage under a high sun. The contrast between the rim and the dark floor is beautiful. The amateur with a fairly large telescope is apt to find himself lured, as so many have been before him, into a specialization that will continue throughout the remainder of his life. Does or does not Plato sometimes exhibit a haze over its floor, visible when the sun is low? Perhaps this ringed plain has been observed more than has any other single feature on the surface of the moon.

Toward the limb to the right, Aristarchus now shows its peculiar relationship to the large disturbed area adjacent to it on the lower right. Beyond that area Seleucus can be seen with its peculiar long ray which, in its branch to the left, becomes the northern boundary of that disturbance. Just right of Aristarchus is the tortuous Schroeter's Valley, the widest of all rills, and nearby is the crater Herodotus.

Plate 6–1 shows Olbers clearly, almost at the limb. If Olbers were not at the limb it certainly would be fully as conspicuous as is Kepler. Because of its location, however, Olbers can be observed only when the librations are unusually favorable, although it can be located at other times because of its ray system. The long ray from Seleucus and a ray from Kepler extend to it (Plate 6–2). Any person who wants to know the nature of lunar rays must become familiar with the oversystem of Copernicus-Kepler-Olbers-Aristarchus, and Seleucus. Possibly the double upper right hand ray from Tycho extended to Kepler and tied in with this oversystem at one time but later had its northern end obliterated by Oceanus Procellarum.

To the south of Olbers and a little farther from the limb is Grimaldi, a small mare with a floor that is one of the darkest areas on the entire satellite. South of Grimaldi is Byrgius, another very bright explosion crater, which would be much better known if it were near the center of the disk.

On Plate 6–2 the disk has lost most of its full moon appearance. Once more Eratosthenes is conspicuous, although Copernicus has not yet faded from its noonday grandeur. The number of observable starlike points scattered over the lunar surface is now smaller because of the lowering altitude of the sun. Ptolemaeus once more is starting to change its appearance toward the wonderful object it was ten days ago.

Between Plates 6–2 and 6–3 Mare Nectaris is at its evening best. On both of these plates the Altai Scarp is dark and the less rough surface between it and Nectaris shows nicely. These plates would give one of the best possible representations of the ridges on the floor to the right if they had been printed to a lesser density, but this of course would have spoiled the detail of the brighter parts. (Plate 10–8 shows such lighter shade in an enlargement.) In the north on Plate 6–3 the terminator is on Posidonius and the time is right for a study of the ridges and craterlets on the floor of Mare Serenitatis that complements the observations made at the time Plate 4–5 was exposed. Turning far to the right we find this to be as satisfactory a time as any to observe the famous right-angle triangle made by the rays of Copernicus, Kepler, and Aristarchus. The plumelike, elementary components show quite well. The serious amateur should observe ray structure at every opportunity and watch the

Plate 6–1. Lick Observatory, 1938 December 8^d 06^h 56^m UT, phase 16.29 days, colongitude 104°. The sunset terminator has almost reached the left shore of Mare Crisium. Farther south Furnerius and Stevinus are beginning to emerge from the glare of light which made observation of their forms very difficult.

Plate 6–2. Lick Observatory, 1937 October 22^d 08^h 03^m UT, phase 17.84 days, colongitude 122°. The left part of the surface has lost the full moon appearance. The right part of the disk still resembles the full moon phase.

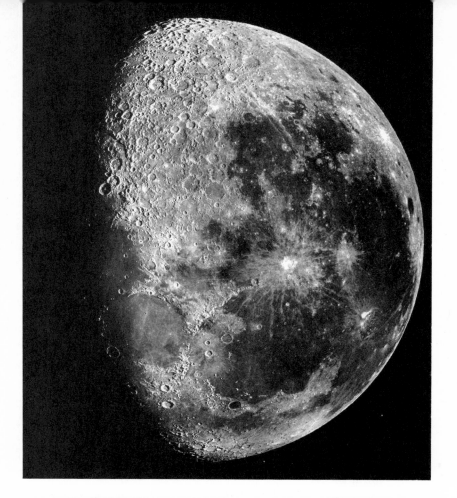

Plate 6–3. Lick Observatory, 1937 October 24^d 13^h 01^m UT, phase 20.05 days, colongitude 149°. The Altai Scarp to the left of the sunset terminator shows dark. In the north the sunset has reached Mare Serenitatis.

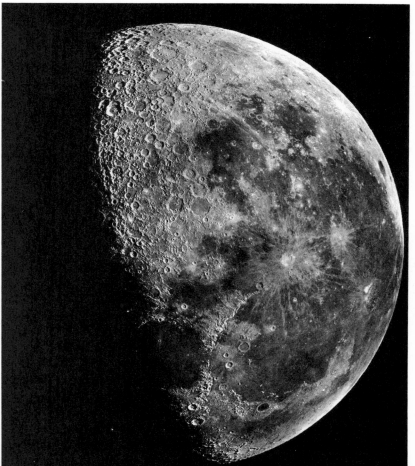

Plate 6–4. Lick Observatory, 1945 October 26^d 13^h 48^m UT, phase 20.35 days, colongitude 156°. Northern end of Altai Scarp on terminator.

changes in it that take place as the height of the sun changes.

In all of his observing the watcher should habitually make notes whenever he is certain of any peculiar detail. If he has the proper skill he should make drawings of all special features, comparing them with what he can see under different lightings. Much that he has observed will prove to be illusory. In my own experience the suggestive power of a visual illusion was demonstrated by observations of the central peak of Eratosthenes. After a series of afternoon observations I was once certain that there was a craterlet at the top of the peak; my craterlet persisted for several days. I soon found, however, that as the direction of the light changes from right to left the craterlet completely disappears. It is all a trick of the shadows. One good visual observing practice is to trace outline major features in pencil on tracing paper placed over an enlarged photograph. The paper then is placed on white cardboard and details are filled in while the observer is at the telescope. At the end of the last century J. N. Krieger employed a practice somewhat similar to this with great success. He used lightly printed photographic enlargements which he completed with pencil. Even good draftsmen will make serious errors of proportion if they do not have a rather complete guide.

On the right hand floor of Serenitatis, at a phase just beyond that of Plate 6–3, Linné is again at its best. The pit craterlet observable at waxing half moon now can be seen again at the top of the ten-mile white mound. Its appearance is entirely different from that under the opposite lighting.

At these phases when Linné is best observable, the Caucasian and Apennine sections of the Imbrian scarp sparkle in the late afternoon sunshine. Their appearance at this time should be contrasted with what it was in the early morning. Also in the Alps, to the north of Mare Imbrium, the Alpine Valley shows nicely. At this phase the row of craterlets along the valley's northern rim is a fine feature to observe with a fair-sized telescope. The craterlets along the southern rim appear most advantageously under a moderately low morning sun. The difference of phase for best observation of these rows probably is due to opposite slopes of the ground outside the valley.

Phase 22 days (Plate 3–2) demands that the visual observer examine Clavius and Maginus for their rim craters, Tycho for detail of its floor, Deslandres, Alphonsus, Ptolemaeus, the craters of the Apennines, the radial valleys outside Aristillus, the left hand floor of Mare Imbrium and the ringed plain Plato. All of these features are lined up on the sunlit side of the terminator.

By 24 days (Plate 6–5) the waning moon has become merely a broad crescent that rises around 2 in the morning. At the terminator in the north the Bay of Rainbows (Sinus Iridum) has begun to disappear into the night. Aristarchus has lost enough of its dazzle to permit observation of the general form of the crater. If conditions are just right the small mountain at the center of its floor may be seen, and there may be a hint of craterlets where the floor joins the inner wall.

On the upper right hand portion of the moon Mare Humorum is at its afternoon best. Just to the left of it and closely paralleling the shoreline, the three "Clefts of Hippalus" are rather easy to observe. On the left hand portion of the mare floor several ridges are easily seen. A half dozen craters, varying from conspicuous to almost unobservable, demonstrate their relationship to the ridges. Several scattered floor craters look very black at the centers of whitish spots. A continental shelf can be seen on the right floor. On the northern shore Gassendi is a splendid object. Its southern floor has sunk, but not sufficiently to have caused degeneration to a mere bay. These features can be more easily observed on the enlargement, Plate 10–5.

South of Mare Humorum the great walled plain Schickard may be observed well when the librations are favorable. Some observers have thought it should be considered as a small mare, but the general shade of its floor does not match that of the maria. To the left of Schickard we can see Schiller, the most eccentrically shaped of all the craterlike formations. The moon's limb in this general area should also be observed because, whenever the librations permit, some high mountains may be seen projected along the limb at this point.

The craters on the extreme right hand portion

Plate 6–5. Lick Observatory, 1938 August 20^d 12^h 47^m UT, phase 24.37 days, colongitude 206°. The sunset terminator is crossing Sinus Iridum and has almost reached Kepler and Mare Humorum. Grimaldi shows dark near the right limb.

Plate 6–6. Lick Observatory, 1936 September 12^d 12^h 57^m UT, phase 26.40 days, colongitude 228°. The sun is setting on Kepler. Aristarchus, close to the terminator, has lost sufficient brightness to permit easy observation of details.

of the floor of Mare Imbrium and those much farther south, where the floors of Mare Nubium and Oceanus Procellarum join, are as important as anything else that can be examined at this or at a later phase. When the moon rises shortly

before dawn, the terminator is moving to the right across these floors, illuminating craterlets and ridges until the crescent shown on Plate 6–6 is reached, about three days before new moon.

7 COPERNICUS THROUGH THE MONTH

The features of the moon testify in general to a relatively quiet period of formation as compared to the geologic activity that has apparently taken place on the earth. This generalization applies to most of the mountain-walled plains such as Deslandres, Ptolemaeus, Clavius, Bailly, Riccioli, and Grimaldi, all of which tend toward a single tint or shade over most of the surface and are therefore very conspicuous only when the sun is low and casts long shadows; it applies to some true craters that are observable under a low or a moderate sun but that practically vanish at noontime.

There is, however, a good-sized minority of violent craters which, although they occupy only a small percentage of the lunar surface, dominate the appearance of the full moon. Such craters seem to indicate explosions far greater than anything of the kind for which evidence remains on the surface of the earth. Among the most famous of this type are Copernicus, Tycho, Kepler, Aristarchus, Olbers, Proclus, and Manilius. Smaller craters of this kind are rather common, and near full moon bright craterlets are numbered in the hundreds. Each of them indicates the site of a very violent local explosion.

The diameter of the floor of Copernicus is about 40 miles and that of its narrow rim is 56 miles. The mean height of the rim is perhaps 12,000 feet, although the rim height above the external plain is much less than it is above the inner surface. (It must be remembered, however, that the degree of uncertainty as to heights and depths on the lunar surface is far greater than one would surmise from a study of the photographs.) Along the rims there are peaks that depart widely from the average level.

Copernicus is conspicuous even when the sun is low, as shown by Plates 7–1 and 7–2. Its shallowness in comparison to its diameter is shown by the fact that the floor, which is entirely dark in Plate 7–1, is almost completely illuminated in Plate 7–2 despite the fact that there is not much difference in altitude of the sun. If we wished to compare Copernicus to a pie pan nine inches in diameter, its depth would be only a third of an inch. When the sun is high, Copernicus exhibits entirely different characteristics from those which it reveals near sunrise and sunset. Plate 7–3, made a day before full moon, shows Copernicus and the lunar landscape for several hundred miles around. Photo-

Plate 7–1. Mt. Wilson and Palomar Observatories, 1956 November 12^d 04^h 04^m
UT, phase 9.47 days, colongitude 20°. Sunrise on Copernicus.

Plate 7–2. Lick Observatory, 1938 July 7^d 04^h 23^m UT, phase 9.30, colongitude 24°. With Plate 7–1 demonstrates shallowness of Copernicus.

Plate 7–3. This photograph, facing due north across the central portion of Copernicus was made at 0:05 U.T., November 24, 1966, using the telephoto lens of Orbiter II. The Orbiter cameras and their techniques are described briefly in Chapter 19. Because of the expanse of sky, this picture, unlike the others in this book, is printed with north up. Orbiter was about 48 km above the surface and roughly 250 km south of the center of Copernicus. The east-west diameter of the part shown is approximately 30 km and is a bit less than a third of the crater's diameter. The rounded mountain in the upper left-hand corner is the ringed plain Gay Lussac. Comparison with Plate 7–2 shows, on each, the row of isolated central mountains. Each picture also reveals that the floor to the north of that row is smoother than it is to the south. The projection of the southern rim of Copernicus against the floor causes it to stand out in sharp contrast. The northern rim, very roughly 100 km farther away, is much less conspicuous. A long, wide, east-west valley can be observed plainly in the northern wall, crossing most of the picture. In even the best-made photographs from the earth's observatories, the valley appears as a mere terrace near the upper part of the wall. Probably it is a graben, formed during the subsidence which modified the original form of the crater.

Lunar students, almost unanimously, believe that at least the initial form of Copernicus was due to the impact of a small asteroid, or giant meteoroid. This excited internal forces which brought about a series of caldera-like collapses that enlarged the floor and left the wall terraces as scars. (See page 117.) We may not know definitely the factors which produced Copernicus until long after man has made contact explorations of the moon.

graphic contrast was chosen for this plate so as to exhibit best the intensity of its ray system, which appears in the plate much as it would for a visual observation at the telescope. This manner of printing the plate "burns out" most small detail, especially near the crater. Plate 7–4, made at nearly the same phase, was exposed and printed to show a very different effect; here deliberate under exposure of the brightest parts of the surface has permitted a print without the "burning out" of the central area. The photograph reveals the actual appearance of Copernicus when the sun is high and therefore minimizes the less bright ray system.

Plates 7–2 and 7–4, different as they are, each give incomplete but equally valid representations of the crater. Shadows are responsible for the general appearance of the first, and the importance of low features is exaggerated in it. This exaggeration is often not recognized as one studies a beautiful photograph, but such recognition and the proper use of it are essential to all serious study. Observations made under a high sun, on the other hand, scarcely hint at such differences of height but, for such craters as Copernicus, they do reveal beautifully the peculiar brightening that develops as the altitude of the sun increases. These high-sun photographs are not as crisp and exciting as those with long shadows, but they are equally important in interpreting the lunar surface. The same principles hold true for the corresponding visual observations.

Plate 7–5 is an intermediate print, made when the sun was moderately high, and exposed and printed to show best the fine structure of the ray system of Copernicus. The many short elementary rays, with their plumes extending radially away from Copernicus, and the complex structure of the great rays, are all vital data for

Plate 7–4. Mt. Wilson and Palomar Observatories, 1958 July 1^d 09^h 27^m UT, phase 14.06 days, colongitude 87°. Short exposure to show detail of Copernicus under a high sun.

an understanding of the complex phenomenon that is Copernicus.

These changes in appearance of Copernicus through the month are almost unbelievable to the novice. It is mainly the existence of such cyclic changes, which are characteristic of many other features also, that has caused the moon to be the favorite of the amateurs.

In Plate 7–1 (colongitude 20°) the whole of the floor of Copernicus and even the tops of the central mountains are dark. The sunlight just strikes the upper part of the inner right hand wall. The outer wall to the left shows terraces, radial valleys, and craterlets.

On the flattish surface to the left of the wall, this sunrise phase begins to show the famous patterns made by rows of confluent craterlets, made conspicuous by long shadows despite their small rise above the general level. At rare and fleeting moments, under the best possible observing conditions, observers using powerful telescopes have reported seeing thousands of such tiny craterlets, especially on the left hand slope.

Among those who have witnessed this phenomenon have been George Ellery Hale, W. W. Campbell, and H. P. Wilkins. Those of us who have observed the moon consistently for a long enough time to have experienced such fractions of a second can never forget these startling flashes of vision. More than anything else they reveal to us how little we know of the fine detail of the lunar surface, despite several centuries of observation.

On Plate 7–2 the altitude of the sun is still low but already most of the floor of Copernicus is illuminated. The three central mountains show as well as at any other time of the month. The shadows exhibit conspicuously the difference between the northern and the southern halves of the floor. Even in the low sunlight, the northern part is seen to be quite smooth, while the southern half is a mass of low hills. The structure of the inner wall becomes apparent at this phase, and will unfold more and more as the altitude of the sun gains moderately. The three famous terraces of the inner wall can be seen. Some

Plate 7–5. Detail of Copernican ray system. See Plate 4–10 for technical details.

Plate 7–6. The Copernicus-Kepler-Aristarchus oversystem of rays. See Plate 3–2 for technical details.

craters appear on the wall. As the lighting changes, different details will in turn reveal their morphological characteristics. The difference in steepness of inner and outer walls is evident at a glance. The inner wall to the left is still dark, but the outer wall to the right is already bright.

On Plate 7–1 everything right of Copernicus was still hidden in night-time blackness. On Plate 7–2 everything for fully a hundred miles to the right is bathed in low sunlight. The resulting long shadows show lines of craterlets, mostly radial to Copernicus but not with the pronounced patterns found to the left. Hortensius is observable to the right of Copernicus and to its north is a group of very low, rounded domes.

These domes are not observable except when the sun is rather low. Many of them, perhaps all, show a tiny, black crater pit at the top. Farther to the north, beyond Milichius, is a dome larger than these of the Hortensius group which shows the crater pit very distinctly. A smaller dome is found quite close to the crater. The frequency and distribution of domes is one of the newer studies of selenography.

It can be assumed that the rays of Copernicus begin to appear half a day after sunrise, although it is almost impossible to set a time with complete accuracy because the density and contrast of even good photographs affect visibility very much. The rays increase their relative brightness until sometime near noon and then hold it for much of the afternoon, fading out be-

73

fore sunset. The best time to observe their fine detail is under a moderate sun. Plate 7–6 was made at the time of the waning half moon. It was printed in an attempt to show the details of the ray system to best advantage. A simultaneous study of it with Plate 7–5 will show many peculiarities in the ray system of Copernicus. One is the fact that the major rays are not radial to Copernicus. The second is that in Mare Imbrium, north of the crater, there are many plume-shaped short rays which are radial to Copernicus. The points of the feathers are toward that crater. In a few cases a craterlet is observable on the pointed end of such an elementary ray and in nearly all cases a brightish spot can be seen there that can be assumed with some confidence to contain a craterlet. Examination of the two major rays extending northward into Mare Imbrium shows that they have a complex structure. Despite overlapping, there are places where this structure can be observed as composed of the elemental plume rays, which are radial although the complex rays are not.

To the left of Copernicus a peculiar feature known as Stadius can be observed, a circle of craterlets elevated very slightly above the general level. Adjoining Stadius on the right is a less regular but similarly enclosed area, and running northward from it is the most conspicuous line of small craters on the moon. The line continues directly into the strongest of the major rays of Copernicus. On the south of Stadius (Plate 7–5) and touching it are the two most peculiar of all rays. They are ovals, one inside the other. Examination of these ovals shows that they, like Stadius, are loci of craterlets. The plumed elemental rays are found throughout their area and other rays, generally radial, extend outward from the perimeters of the ovals.

On the upper right, the Copernican ray system is much complicated by the additional presence of rays from Kepler. Featherlike components belonging to each of the craters are observable.

Plate 7–7 was made just before sunset and reveals the same sort of detail as was shown in the early morning. Eratosthenes, which had almost disappeared under the high sun, is almost exactly on the terminator and is as conspicuous as it was at sunrise. The hexagonal shape of the rim of Copernicus shows nicely at this phase, contrasting with the nearly circular shape of the floor. The contrast between this picture of the rim and that of Plate 7–4 is one of the most startling to be observed on the moon.

The Copernican phenomena which have been described are the principal ones to consider in any study of the nature and origin of Copernicus. A satisfactory hypothesis may not necessarily demand the existence of all of them but it must not forbid any of them. The data for Copernicus and for all other similar craters must be more or less formally combined before any valuable study is possible. Even then the hypotheses of candid and able selenologists are contradictory. These disagreements may persist even after lunar explorers have actually visited the site; after all there is still disagreement about many of the features of the earth to which geologists have relatively easy access!

Plate 7–7. Mt. Wilson and Palomar Observatories, 1955 October 9^d 11^h 58^m UT, phase 23.24 days, colongitude 188. Late afternoon on Copernicus.

8 TYCHO THROUGH THE MONTH

It frequently happens that a person looking at the full moon through a telescope for the first time exclaims "Look at the north pole!" What prompts the exclamation is the view of Tycho and its rays as shown by Plates 5–2 and 8–3. It looks amazingly like the polar circle with radiating lines of longitude. Even an observer who knows perfectly well that the poles of planets are not marked by any external signs and that meridians are artificial lines drawn for convenience on maps is struck by the similarity.

Tycho and Copernicus are competitors for pre-eminence among the craterlike features of the lunar surface. When the sun is low Copernicus definitely outclasses all other ringed plains, but when the sun is high Tycho is so magnificent that even the great maria scarcely rival it. Copernicus has the advantage of being situated in one of the dark, smooth maria. Tycho is in one of the roughest bright areas of the moon. Around it are great mountain-walled plains (Plates 8–1 and 8–2), some of them with diameters more than twice that of Tycho. When the sun is low the shadows cause these walled plains to stand out in majesty. The surfaces of nearly all the walled plains are composed of rock of one shade, so when the sun is high and shadows are short they almost disappear. But at such times Tycho

and its brother ringed plains brighten far more than the surrounding areas, and divert our primary attention from the other features.

In Plate 8–1 Tycho is exactly on the sunrise terminator. Only the crater rim is illuminated; all of the interior part, including the central mountain, is in darkness. Crater rims always are higher than are any central mountains that may exist. The rough features to the left of Tycho are emphasized by their long shadows. To the north of Tycho, toward the bottom of Plate 8–1, is Deslandres, the largest of all the mountain-walled plains, and one that is certainly older than most of the other craterlike enclosures on the moon. On this plate it is observed as one of the most conspicuous of all features, but its walls are so low that at even a day's phase later one must look carefully to find it. Plate 8–2 shows within Deslandres an intensely bright spot that is related to the Tychonian ray system. This spot is bright, however, even when it is near the terminator with the sun too low for Tycho's rays to be observed. It is called "Cassini's Bright Spot" because of the assertion by that astronomer, three centuries ago, that he had observed a cloud there and that a short while later a "new formation" first became visible. It is interesting that both Neison and Goodacre insisted mistakenly that

Plate 8–1. Sunrise on Tycho and Deslandres. See Plate 4–6 for technical details.

Plate 8–2. Tycho and Deslandres in early morning. See Plate 4–10 for technical details.

Plate 8–3. Details of ray system near Tycho. See Plate 5–2 for technical details.

the feature does not exist. A small crater (Plate 8–2) is easily observable throughout a good part of the lunar day. Undoubtedly Cassini was mistaken concerning the seventeenth-century origin of the object, but the later students must have made insufficient observations, and those at the wrong time of the month. This is a very easy error for even an experienced observer to make concerning features about which he has only casual interest. The bright spot is useful in locating Deslandres when the sun is high. Plate 8–8, made in the afternoon, exhibits the craterlet almost as beautifully as does Plate 8–2, made in the morning.

Plate 8–2 was made at a phase only a day later than that of the preceding picture, but a significant change has taken place. All of the floor of Tycho is illuminated, giving proof that, as in the case of Copernicus, its depth is small in comparison to its diameter. Among the mountain-walled plains Deslandres has become almost invisible and changes in others, such as Maginus, are noticeable. The point to remember is that the mountainous areas of the moon are in general less rugged than observations near the terminator would indicate. Tycho is much less deep in relation to its diameter than even a shallow pie pan, and the walled plains such as Maginus are still flatter. A man standing at the center of Clavius or of Ptolemaeus would have no idea that he was even within an enclosure because of his point of view.

On Plate 8–3, made five days after sunrise on Tycho, the whole area is entirely unrecognizable. (Plate 10–4, which has been corrected for foreshortening, well may be studied simultaneously with Plate 8–3.) It is possible at this phase to make exposures of negatives and photographic prints in such a way that to some extent they restore to visibility the details of the central portion of Tycho, but mere exposure cannot restore the lost mountain-walled plains, which depend almost exclusively on shadows for their visibility. At first glance Plate 8–3 shows Tycho as a circular white blob with great, almost radial, bright spokes. It may be observed next that the image of Tycho is scalloped, where craters and parts of craters exist on its rim. Immediately outside the rim is a dark area into which the rays scarcely intrude. Neison wrote of this area as a plateau but an examination of various photographs indicates that it is more likely a slight depression. Nine of the ray spokes exist if we consider the double one toward the lower right as two and also include the rather indefinite one that bisects the great gap to the right. Between the major rays, we find the same sort of elemental plume rays as around Copernicus. Unlike the major rays, they are radial. The major ray toward the lower left corner of Plate 8–3 is especially notable. Even a casual examination

will show that it ends before the edge of the picture and is replaced by a closely parallel ray that starts about half-way between Tycho and the edge. Plate 8–4 has been made, by use of a high-contrast emulsion and proper choice of exposure time, to show the structure of this ray, which is primarily a series of bright craters. A fuller discussion of this ray belongs properly to a study of the nature of the lunar rays.

Plates 8–5, 8–6, and 8–7 are enlargements of a photograph of Tycho and its surroundings made after the intensity of the rays has decreased in the late afternoon sunshine. A beautiful arc of small craters can be seen on the lower left hand portion of the floor, Plate 8–7. A partially sunken oval area breaks the wall slightly at the lower right hand portion of the rim and therefore cannot be older than Tycho. The rather flat floors of the walled plains just to the lower left

Plate 8–4. Mt. Wilson and Palomar Observatories, 1958 August 1ᵈ 07ʰ 22ᵐ UT, phase 15.53 days, co-longitude 105°. Kodak IV–N plate with infrared filter for extreme contrast. Details of Tycho's greatest left-hand ray.

Plate 8–5. Mt. Wilson and Palomar Observatories, 1955 October 8^d 12^h 53^m UT, phase 22.27 days, colongitude 176°. Southern area of moon at third quarter.

Plate 8–6. Enlargement of Plate 8–5 to show Tycho in late afternoon.
See Plate 8–5 for technical details.

Plate 8–7. Detail of Tycho and surroundings. See Plate 8–5 for technical details.

Plate 8–8. Fading of Tycho's rays. See Plate 6–2 for technical details.

of Tycho contain about two dozen lines of crater-lets which are radial to it. These should be compared to similar lines near Copernicus (Plates 7–1—7–7). Plate 8–8, made under a moderately high afternoon sun, has been printed to emphasize the narrow bright rim of Tycho. At both the inner and outer edges of the rim the slopes appear to begin so suddenly that they indicate a sharp breakaway. At various places both within and outside the bright ring can be seen the rim craters that are an almost universal accompaniment of the large craters, whether or not they are sites of violent explosions. The detail of this picture is different in almost every way from that of Plate 8–5. It would almost appear that features of entirely different shape had replaced most of those shown on the latter plate. As in

the case of Copernicus the reason is rather obvious: Plate 8–5 depends mainly on shadows and roughness but Plate 8–8 depends primarily on variations in the reflectivity of the surface. The two plates correlate quite well insofar as the truly explosive features are concerned; the quiescent features, on the other hand, display almost no correlation.

Plate 8–9 advances the time to sunset, with the central peak casting its long shadow all the way to the inner left hand wall. Tycho is no more conspicuous than it was at sunrise, but during the day its radical changes in appearance have furnished data that are valuable for interpreting not only the origin of the violently explosive craters but also the lunar surface as a whole.

83

Plate 8–9. Mt. Wilson and Palomar Observatories, 1958 July 9^d 10^h 40^m UT, phase 22.11 days, colongitude 185°. Setting sun on Tycho.

9 SUNSET ON PTOLEMAEUS

The frequent observer of the moon, whether professional or amateur, is generally enthralled by the fast-changing panorama of shadows at sunrise and sunset. The lack of atmosphere on the moon is the cause of the striking contrasts at these times. There is almost no portion of the lunar disk where light and darkness mingle and negate each other; each point is either in full sunlight or in blackness relieved only by reflections from neighboring elevations. The sky is totally dark and there is no twilight.

The shadows of mountains, ridges, and low elevations unobservable except under angular light carry much valuable information. The four photographs reproduced here as Plate 9–1 illustrate the rapidity of the change in appearance. One would expect that the changes would be slow; after all, the sun shines on any point on the moon for more than two weeks at a stretch. But the interval between the first and last of these pictures was only 79 minutes, a short enough time for an amateur to observe continuously. The largest of the craterlike formations is the hexagonal walled plain Ptolemaeus. Its floor is approximately 90 miles in diameter and ordinarily it is considered very flat, except for the crater Lyot, which is conspicuous. Alphonsus is the smaller feature above Ptolemaeus. Walled

plains are depressed areas in mountainous regions. Typically they exhibit little or no explosive action. They are not truly surrounded by walls but rather by the rough mountains of the area. There are often numerous high peaks on these mountains but at some places there are great gaps.

In the first picture with the setting sun still illuminating most of the floor the shape of the shadows indicates a gap in the right hand rim of Ptolemaeus. Even in the last photograph, where the sun scarcely touches the floor, there is no shadow at all at the gap; the break in the wall is obviously complete. Above the gap (south) is a very complex mountain mass with the appearance of an almost unbelievably sharp, high peak. However, much of this steepness is merely the illusion caused by the exaggeration made by shadows from a low sun. During the short interval of time represented by this sequence of photographs the tip of the shadow of this peak moves to the left across the floor, until in the last picture it has merged with the blackness that has engulfed the left hand portion of the plain. This general darkening to the left is caused by the curvature of the moon's surface, which shows nicely on the central plain.

On the floor of Ptolemaeus nearly two hun-

85

dred tiny craters are observable under proper conditions. Almost none of them shows in these pictures. In addition to these craters there are perhaps three dozen fairly large but extremely shallow depressions that are usually referred to as "saucers." Only three or four of them can be seen when the sun is high, but in the grazing sun they stand out in considerable detail, as they do in these pictures. In the upper right hand portion of the floor is an almost perfect circle of nine of the saucers. Seven of the nine can be observed in the first picture, but by the time the last picture was taken nearly all of them were hidden by the shadow of the wall.

Examination of the area lit by sunlight streaming through the gap in the rim makes it clear that progressively more and more of the roughness of the floor becomes visible as the sun nears the horizon. Not only are the saucers seen, but there are ridges and valleys, generally tangent to the saucers. Such features have too little elevation to cast shadows except when the sun is practically on the horizon.

Students of the moon are uncertain of the cause of these shallow depressions. Perhaps they are "ghosts," remnants of old-time craters that came into existence soon after Ptolemaeus took form, while its floor was still so plastic that they were almost destroyed by the subsidence of their material. More probably most of them are ghosts of old craters which existed here before Tycho came into being. Whatever the cause may have been, it was apparently an important factor in forming some of these great walled plains.

Plate 9–1. Mt. Wilson and Palomar Observatories, 1955 November 7^d 11^h 38^m UT; 12^h 04^m; 12^h 32^m; 12^h 57^m; phases 22.67 to 22.73 days, colongitudes 181° to 182°. Sunset on Ptolemaeus.

10 THE NATURE OF THE LUNAR MARIA

The origin of the maria, like so much else in connection with the mysterious satellite, is controversial. The hypotheses fall roughly into three classes, with minor variations and crossovers. Each of them is supported by able students and anyone who wishes to know the moon must be familiar with all three.

The three types of hypotheses are the following:

1. The maria were caused by collisions with asteroids, the molten rock which produced the rather flat surfaces resulting from the collisions.

2. The maria may have resulted from such collisions but the molten rock, at least in part, existed previously on the moon.

3. The molten rock came from beneath the surface of the moon as a result of great surface-wide convulsions. If collisions with asteroids did occur they did no more than trigger those convulsions. If the convulsions were of a tidal nature they may themselves have produced at least part of the molten rock.

Any hypothesis concerning the formation of the maria must explain—or at least not contradict—the following known facts about the seas:

1. The surfaces of the maria approximate flat plains more closely than do any other large areas of the moon.

2. The maria are the largest of all lunar features; some are visible even to the naked eye.

3. The maria are much darker than the general area of the lunar surface. Only smooth floors within certain craters and a very few small mountainous areas reflect so little light.

4. The larger maria are interconnected.

5. Long, very low ridges are common on the surfaces of the maria. Two of the systems are more than 800 miles long and are significantly close to meridional in direction.

6. Some large "craters" and a good many small ones appear on the surfaces.

7. The boundaries between the maria and the adjoining rough areas are usually cliffs. Many of these are very high and some are several hundred miles long.

8. In general, the "seaward" walls of large craters that touch the shores of maria are either lower than the landward walls or are entirely missing.

9. On the floors of most of the maria there are "ghosts," which appear to be craters that are entirely or almost entirely submerged.

Plate 10–1. Mt. Wilson and Palomar Observatories, 1956 July 30^d 11^h 29^m UT, phase 22.22 days, colongitude 183°. Floor of Mare Nubium.

Plate 10–2. Details of Straight Wall and surroundings before sunset.
See Plate 10–1 for technical details.

10. Adjoining some of the maria are large "marshy" areas. These are usually found where the shoreline cliffs are low or entirely missing.

11. "Continental shelves" are common inside the periphery of maria, the floors deepening suddenly some distance from the shoreline. The deeper areas in the floors have sharp boundaries.

12. The northern shores of four of the great maria—Imbrium, Serenitatis, Tranquillitatis, and Foecunditatis—lie very nearly on a great circle of the lunar surface.

13. Four fifths of the maria surfaces on the visible side of the moon are found in the right hand hemisphere.

14. Photographs taken by the Soviet satellite, Lunik II, show that the far side of the moon has little mare surface.

The characteristics of some of the better known and more noteworthy maria are described in the following paragraphs.

Mare Nubium (Plates 10–1—10–3). This mare is interesting chiefly because of the "Straight Wall" and the numerous ghosts found on its surface. The Straight Wall is a cliff about 80 miles long and perhaps 1,000 feet high forming one section of the left hand shore of Nubium. In the afternoon (Plates 10–1 and 10–2) it shows as a bright line but under the morning sun (Plate 10–3) it appears as a dark line. To the left of the wall are seen half of the boundary, and the corresponding floor portion, of an old mountain-walled plain of huge size. To the right is the mare floor. Under a low sun the almost destroyed remnants of the right hand wall are visible. In the rough ground to the south of the mare is Deslandres (Plates 10–1 and 10–3), another old walled plain of nearly the same size as the partially destroyed one at the Straight Wall. Deslandres can be observed as an integral feature only when the sun is very low; otherwise its walls do not cast enough shadow to exhibit its form. Plate 10–1 also shows the ghost of a third plain of roughly the same size touching the Straight Wall plain on its north. This plain is so nearly

Plate 10–3. Mt. Wilson and Palomar Observatories, 1954 November 4^d 02^h 47^m UT, phase 8.37 days, colongitude 11°. Sunrise on the Straight Wall.

Plate 10–4. Correction of foreshortening near Tycho. The technique used is explained in the Appendix.

destroyed that it can be recognized only by the approximately circular black area. These huge plains, dim reminders out of the evolutionary past, certainly belong to an earlier stage of lunar history. At no other place does one find stronger evidence suggesting that the maria were formed by a caldera type of collapse of surface area.

On the floor of Nubium (Plate 10–1) is a string of three almost engulfed ghosts of old craters. They extend northward from $x = 87$; $y = 93$ of the map, Plate 3–2. Just to the left of the northernmost of the three is a larger ghost, the wall of which is almost at the level of the mare floor. A peninsula of high ground runs southward from the Copernican area to end in the vicinity of these ghosts. Two of the craters on the peninsula, Fra Mauro and Bonpland, have almost lost their walls but probably they have not vanished sufficiently to be classed as ghosts. The crater Pitatus (Plate 10–1) touches the southern floor of the mare with the usual result: its seaward wall is much lower than the rest.

Plate 10–4 is a view of Mare Nubium and Mare Humorum, corrected for foreshortening by proper projection of a photograph on a globe. The method and the story of its development are told in the appendix. This print is reproduced by courtesy of Dr. Harold C. Urey. It shows the two maria and the southern part of Oceanus Procellarum with little distortion. It also shows the mare-like patches to the south of Humorum. These areas are closely related to the great gap on the right in the major ray system of Tycho.

If Mare Nubium in its present condition were the result of a great explosion caused by either internal or impact forces it is unlikely that the ghosts could have remained. There would also be no reason to expect the low northern wall of Pitatus and the sinking at the Straight Wall.

If Nubium resulted from a general upwelling, great enough for molten rock to overflow an area which had undergone a caldera-like sinking, all of the observed data would appear to be reasonable. This observation of cause does not pre-

91

Plate 10–5. Mare Humorum in late afternoon.
See Plate 6–5 for technical details.

Plate 10–6. Sunrise on Mare Nectaris.
See Plate 4–3 for technical details.

clude the hypothesis that a small asteroid or a large meteorite may have struck near the center of the region and acted merely as a trigger to produce a sinking in an area that was already unstable.

Mare Humorum (Plates 10–4, 10–5). This small sea adjoins Nubium on the right. It is one of the more circular of the maria. The floor shows a distinct continental shelf. Left of the central part of the floor there is a beautiful, irregular, and complex north-south thrust ridge, so low that it is visible only when the sun is near the horizon. It exhibits a relationship to craterlets.

Humorum is notable for its large craters with walls broken at the shoreline. On the left hand shore Hippalus has become a mere bay with a system of three strong parallel rills running from lower left to upper left of it. A continuation of

these rills can be seen beyond a mountainous area directly to the south. They reach Ramsden, which itself has a fine rill system that can be seen faintly on Plate 10–5.

On the southern shore, as shown by this plate, Lee and Doppelmayer have very badly broken seaward walls. Directly left of Doppelmayer is a fine ghost. Lee is located within the ghost of an even larger crater, so badly broken that it has not been named. On the northern shore of Humorum is Gassendi, one of the most noted of the ringed plains. Its southern wall is lower than the others and at one point is completely broken. This mare tells in a less spectacular manner the same story as Nubium.

Mare Nectaris (Plates 10–6—10–8). Plate 10–6 exhibits Nectaris and its surroundings when the sun is rising on the floor to the left. A great cliff runs southward from Gutenberg to become part of the shoreline on the left. Just inside the floor is one of the most conspicuous continental shelves to be found on the moon. On the southern shore the sun just strikes the crest of Fracastorius, one of the largest of the walled plains. At this phase the very low seaward wall does not show and it appears to be a great bay. Plates 10–7 and 10–8 show Beaumont, another such baylike crater on the right hand shore. The floor also exhibits a combined ridge and continental shelf inside the shore on the right. At the lower right is Theophilus, a great ringed plain. Plate 10–7 shows that the left rim of Theophilus is lower than the one away from the mare.

The chief interest in Nectaris in connection with the evolution of the lunar surface lies in the Altai Scarp which is far to the right of the shoreline. In Plate 10–7 the rising sun strikes the crest of the scarp, which extends for several hundred miles like an arc centered on Mare Nectaris. This plate shows a partial parallel ridge between the scarp and the mare. There were three major sinkings in the development of Mare Nectaris. Under a low afternoon sun (Plate 10–8) the scarp is dark, proving that it is not a ridge. Both of these photographs show the modification of the surface between the scarp and the sea. They also show the long ridge on the right floor, which is higher on its left than on its right slope.

One might contend that some scarps, such as those of the Apennines, were caused primarily by melting at the line where the break occurred, but such a hypothesis could not possibly apply to the Altai Scarp. Mare Nectaris tells exactly the same story as do Mare Nubium and Mare Humorum.

Mare Crisium (Plates 10–9—10–10). This, the most completely enclosed of the larger maria, resembles the largest of the typical mountain-walled plains more closely than do any of the other maria. A continental shelf parallels almost

Plate 10–7. Sunrise on the Altai Scarp. See Plate 4–4 for technical details.

Plate 10–8. Lick Observatory, 1940 August 22^d 12^h 48^m UT, phase 18.69 days, colongitude 142°. Altai Scarp in the late afternoon.

Plate 10–9. Ghosts and continental shelves on Mare Crisium. See Plate 4–3 for technical details.

Plate 10–10. The floor of Oceanus Procellarum, showing the 40-km-diameter crater Marius near the upper right corner. Exposed through the wide-angle camera lens of Orbiter II, 1966 November 25. See Plate 3–24. (Photo: NASA.)

the whole of the shoreline on the left. Plate 10–9 shows, just right of the center, an elongated sunken area that occupies perhaps a fifth of the floor. The "half-craters" on the shoreline of the mare are too numerous and too conspicuous to require individual comments. The plate shows also a lacy network of ghosts, especially on the northern part of the floor. Some of them even cast a hint of shadow when the sun is very close to the horizon. At no place do we find evidence that the plain was produced by an explosion, either internal or impact. The floor appears to have sunk far below its mountainous surroundings and to have been flooded.

The best terrestrially made photographs show many domes in the region to the north of Marius. In those pictures they appear as smooth and rounded, except that many show a craterlet in the top (pages 73, 113, and Chapter 13). Plate 7–2 shows them nicely in the Copernican area. On the far more open scale of Plate 10–10, all are seen to be rough, often with tiny craterlets scattered over the surface. At the center of this plate is a typical pair. Three have been partially

merged directly below them. In the lower right-hand corner is another beautiful pair. The upper left quadrant of the picture is "full" of them. In the lower right-hand corner, a section of the long diagonal ridge is seen to be composed of 18 contiguous craterlets. Probably the crater Marius is a caldera although it may have had an impact origin. However, a large majority of the other observable features are due to endoforces.

We cannot be certain, but possibly it would be disastrous for astronauts to land on a dome. Contrariwise, the area between a separated pair, such as those at the center of Plate 10–10, would appear, at a wild guess, to be almost ideal, if the landing site can be controlled precisely enough.

The Maria on the Left (Plates 10–11 and 10–12). Both photographs show Maria Crisium, Marginis, Smythii, Spumans, Undarum, Foecunditatis, and Tranquillitatis, and Plate 10–11 also shows Serenitatis and Nectaris. Smythii resembles Crisium but is badly distorted by foreshortening even in Plate 10–11. Despite the unavoidable poor quality of a first picture, Plate 18–1, the Russian picture of the far side of the moon gives

Plate 10–11. The left hand Maria partly corrected for foreshortening (see Appendix).

Plate 10–12. The left hand Maria. See Plate 4–8 for technical details.

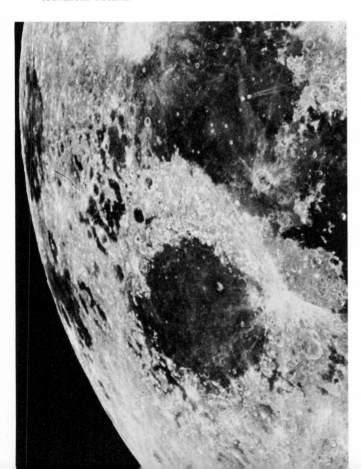

us a better understanding of both Maria Smythii and Marginis. The first five of the maria definitely appear to be interrelated. Spumans and Undarum are small mare areas which seem to have congealed before they could completely merge. The same phenomenon is seen at the upper left hand limb in the case of Mare Australe (Plate 4–11). When inspected casually, the whole area gives the impression of an interrupted subsidence which, if it had been completed, would have produced a single mare as large as Mare Imbrium. One tends to get the feeling that a gigantic force was acting at once on the whole of the lunar surface, a force which apparently had its maximum intensity in the lower right quadrant of the visible surface. All maria seem to be related. If the force was weaker near the left limb, upheavals and subsequent sinkings would have produced here lesser modifications of the original surface than they did in the Imbrian area. The hypothesis of a trigger impact is less satisfactory in the lower left hand quadrant than it is for other parts of the surface.

Mare Serenitatis and Mare Tranquillitatis (Plates 10–11—10–16). These seas are larger than any of the preceding ones. Mare Serenitatis is isolated except for three gaps, one on the south to Tranquillitatis, one on the right to Imbrium, and a small irregular one on the north to an extension of Mare Frigoris. Plates 10–13 and 10–14 exhibit several interesting features of the left hand floor of Serenitatis. One of these is a fine continental shelf. Farther in on the floor are the great north-south ridges that merge at their northern and southern ends and which are a continuation of the ridge system of the right hand portion of Tranquillitatis, Plate 10–17. Plate 10–14 shows a beautiful row of half-craters along the southern shore extending left from Menelaus. Along the left shore, Le Monnier has lost all of its seaward wall to become a bay. Just to the north of Le Monnier is Posidonius, god of the seas, fittingly represented by one of the greatest of the ringed plains. Its right wall is almost broken at one point and it duplicates almost perfectly the situation of Gassendi at Humorum and Pitatus at Nubium. Few ghosts are found on the floor of Serenitatis.

A remarkable feature of Mare Serenitatis is the very dark edging just inside the shore line, well shown by Plates 10–14, 3–13, 3–14. The edg-

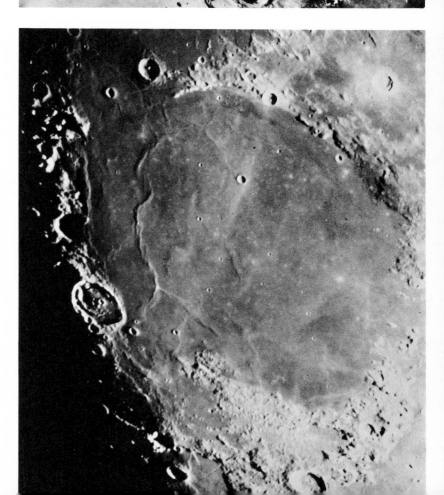

Plate 10–13. Mt. Wilson and Palomar Observatories, 1957 May 6^d 04^h 49^m UT, phase 6.20 days, colongitude 351°. Sunrise terminator on Mare Serenitatis.

Plate 10–14. Mt. Wilson and Palomar Observatories, 1954 July 20^d 09^h 31^m UT, phase 19.88 days, colongitude 148°. Sunset on left shore of Mare Serenitatis.

Plate 10–15. Mt. Wilson and Palomar Observatories, 1958 July 7^d 10^h 32^m UT, phase 20.11 days, colongitude 161°. Right hand part of Mare Serenitatis and the crater pit on Linné.

Plate 10–16. Mt. Wilson and Palomar Observatories, made one minute after Plate 10–15, using Kodak II–0 plate sensitive to blue-green and shorter wavelengths. Covers same area as Plate 10–15.

ing extends through the gap into Tranquillitatis, where in many places the floor is of the same dark shade. From the analogy of terrestrial lava flows, one might guess that the edging is a result of oozing of molten rock after the main process of evolution had been completed. The idea has been advanced, because of the extension to the south, that the edging indicates a flow of lava from Tranquillitatis into Serenitatis. Although it is possible that such a flow did occur, it must have been independent of the edging, as is indicated by the presence of the edging along both right and left hand shores.

The ray systems of Menelaus and Bessel (Plate 10–14) prove them to be younger than the mare. On the right hand floor of Serenitatis is found Linné (Plates 10–15, 10–16), the most controversial of all the craters on the moon. See Chapter 16. The low altitude of the sun when these pictures were made reveals the exceptionally fine ridge system found on the right hand floor.

Tranquillitatis (Plate 3–10) is a large mare with a very irregular and generally low shoreline. To its left is a large, partly blocked channel which connects it to Mare Foecunditatis. To the south a strait connects it to Mare Nectaris. Right of it is the jumbled, partly marshy, area north of Ptolemaeus. The right hand part of the floor (Plate 10–17) shows a section of perhaps the finest ridge system on the whole moon. It extends from Theophilus north through Tranquillitatis to connect with the system in Serenitatis and thus form one of the most spectacular features of the moon. This closely meridional ridge system, more than 800 miles long, and another system which almost duplicates it in Oceanus Procellarum, surely cannot be the results of localized impact forces.

Mare Imbrium (Plates 10–18—10–24). Except for Oceanus Procellarum, Mare Imbrium

Plate 10–17. Mt. Wilson and Palomar Observatories, 1954 July 20^d 09^h 31^m UT, phase 19.88 days, colongitude 148°. Kodak 33 plate, no filter. Ridge system north from Theophilus, through Mare Tranquillitatis into Mare Serenitatis.

Plate 10–18. Sunset at left shore of Mare Serenitatis. See Plate 3–2 for technical details.

Plate 10–19. Portion of Plate 10–18. Detail of left floor of Mare Imbrium.

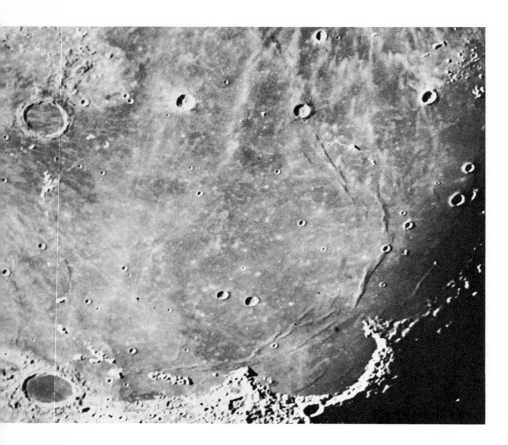

Plate 10–20. The ridges of right hand part of Mare Imbrium. See Plate 4–10 for technical details.

(Plate 10–18) is the largest of the maria. Plates 10–19 and 10–20 show the great central ridge ring of Mare Imbrium, a roughly circular low ridge around the center of the mare. At places it is so low that it can be observed only for a short time after sunrise and before sunset. The diameter is great enough that the right and left sides must be observed at different phases. On the south it includes Timocharis and Lambert. The rays of the former prove that crater to be younger than the mare. Plate 10–20 shows this area and the right side of the ring. Plate 10–21 is an enlargement of the region near Lambert and shows that crater in the lower right. Just before reaching Lambert the ridge is joined by the principal northern rays from Copernicus. Often the statement is made that rays are not elevated. The statement perhaps is true of most but not of all rays: Plate 10–21 shows that these Copernican rays lie along a ridge. From Lambert the ridge continues to Caroline Herschel and then turns to the lower left to block the entrance to Sinus

Iridum. Next it touches the Straight Range, then continues left to include the Teneriffe Mountains (Plate 10–19) and the separate mountain Pico. At Pico it turns southward once more to Spitzbergen, a small mountain range north of Archimedes, then extends to the upper right toward Timocharis. This is a complex ridge, and not the boundary of a sunken area such as may be found, for example, in Mare Crisium and in Sinus Aestuum.

Perhaps a third of Imbrium lies within the ridge system. This central area is very different from the remainder of Imbrium and from the other maria. The ring in most places has the general appearance of being an outward, compression wave of molten rock from some center of disturbance. If in any lunar area there has been asteroidal bombardment amounting to more than triggering action in the formation of a mare, it has been here.

Plate 10–22 shows that a useful picture need not be a pretty one. The highlights are so dense

Plate 10–21. Mt. Wilson and Palomar Observatories, 1955 October 9^d 11^h 25^m UT, phase 23.21 days, colongitude 188°. Detail of ridges in right hand part of Mare Imbrium.

Plate 10–22. Mt. Wilson and Palomar Observatories, 1958 October 28^d 05^h 13^m UT, phase 15.34 days, colongitude 97°. Kodak IV–N plate with infrared filter. The asteroidal impact area.

Plate 10–23. Mt. Wilson and Palomar Observatories, 1958 August 1ᵈ 08ʰ 16ᵐ UT, phase 15.57 days, colongitude 105°. Kodak IV–N plate. This plate was printed longer than Plate 10–22 to show detail in brightest regions.

on the negative that they are merely white paper on the print. The plate used was a Kodak IV-N infrared, which is supposed to be too contrasty to have any value in lunar photography. It was exposed only a half-day after the full moon phase. However, the high contrast brings out certain types of detail on the dark mare floor better than any other plate available for this area. As a result, several hours have been spent in almost memorizing the story it tells. The greatest difference between it and other pictures is the clarity with which it exhibits a large triangular area within the central ring, showing it to be distinctly darker than the remainder of the floor. This is the approximate area pinpointed by several astronomers as the postulated site of an asteroidal impact, which they suggest was the cause of the mare. We can be quite certain that an asteroid, perhaps one belonging to the earth-moon system, did strike in this place.

Before we fully accept this hypothesis of the origin of Mare Imbrium we must look at other features of the picture. To the south of the impact area Copernican rays are seen traversing several hundred miles of the mare floor. They stop at the southern boundary of this darkest area. When Copernicus came into existence the southern part of the floor could not have been extremely hot, for if it had been it would not exhibit the rays. Certainly the molten rock must have been hot enough originally to prevent the formation of such rays. It seems quite certain, therefore, that the southern part of the floor of Imbrium is considerably older than Copernicus. There are two possible explanations for the stoppage of the rays at the dark area. The first is that the outer mare area had cooled very much before Copernicus was formed but that the actual area of the earlier impact still remained very hot. This is certainly a reasonable explanation. The

Plate 10–24. Correction of foreshortening at Sinus Iridum (see Appendix).

other is that the impact occurred after there was much cooling of the mare surface and that the impact, instead of creating the mare, merely produced profound modifications within it. Which of these is true must be decided from a study of the whole lunar surface.

Other interesting features exist, some of them best shown by underexposing a photograph of the full moon, as was done for Plate 10–23. In it Mare Frigoris is seen as a long series of small connecting seas, separated from Imbrium by the Caucasian-Alpine-Iridum island. Frigoris parallels the northern shore of Imbrium and appears to have been formed at the same epoch as that larger sea. The long island was an area of resistance. Another such area of resistance is the partially sunken area extending from the Apennine scarp to Archimedes (Plates 10–18, 10–22, 10–23). On photographs of the full moon a glance at Archimedes should serve as a warning against accepting any one observation in deciding the nature of a lunar feature. In these pictures Archimedes appears definitely to have a broken left wall. Pictures made when the shadows are longer, as for example in Plate 10–19, show that no indication of any such break exists. The one phase emphasizes differences of shade of the surface; the other exaggerates the effects of differences of elevation.

Aristillus and Timocharis appear under a high sun (Plates 10–22 and 10–23) to consist mainly of a ring of bright dots with another such dot at the center of the ring. Under a lower lighting they are shown to be typically fine examples of explosive craters, and ringed plains. Study of them at different phases proves the bright spots to be craters or in some cases half-craters around the rims.

Outside the central ring Mare Imbrium follows the same evolutionary pattern as do the other maria. To the left is the Apennine scarp, far the grandest to be found. The scarps continue northward as the right boundary of the Caucasus Mountains and to the right as the northern boundary of the Carpathians. A broad peninsula to Archimedes (Plates 10–18, 10–22, and 10–23) is, apparently, composed of partially sunken fragments of the original Apennines. In the neighboring area there is much "marshy" ground. Inside this left hand portion are found detached islands of resistance. Mount Pico is a remnant of

an old and very large craterlike ring. Everywhere in its left hand area Imbrium appears to follow the usual pattern of mare evolution and shows nothing of a nature different from the other maria.

The northern shore of Imbrium (Plates 10–18, 10–22, and 10–23) reveals a less precipitous scarp than the Apennine one. On this northern shore is Sinus Iridum, the Bay of Rainbows. Some able advocates of the impact formation of the mare have postulated that this is the site of the initial impact of the asteroid. But when foreshortening is corrected (Plate 10–24) by photographing one of the Wright globes, the bay is seen to be deep rather than shallow, its boundary derived from two sides, and parts of two others, of an old hexagonal mountain-walled plain. The history was almost the same as that of the Straight Wall (Plates 10–1—10–3).

Sinus Aestuum is a large bay just south of Eratosthenes. On Plate 10–18 its floor exhibits one of the finest sunken areas to be found on the moon.

What, in sum, is the origin of the maria? To the facts which have been presented in this chapter and to many more like them, which have been omitted because of lack of space, must be added special studies of peculiar areas. The evidence of the area to the south of Mare Humorum, with its mare-like features that have almost obliterated Tycho's major rays through an arc of fully 120°; the wild marshy area south from Serenitatis, right from Tranquillitatis and extending almost to Ptolemaeus; the long, complex Mare Frigoris and the general mare areas—all seem to demand hypotheses along these lines:

1. The maria and their plains have resulted from a great, convulsive force acting on the surface of the moon, followed by sinkings and the outflow of molten rock.

2. Meteorites and asteroids striking in unstable areas may have had a trigger effect, initiating the process described in the preceding paragraph, but they cannot by themselves have produced the maria in the form in which they now exist.

3. The present form of that part of Mare Imbrium which is within its central ring is an exception to the foregoing hypothesis.

4. The maria, with some possible exceptions, are younger than the mountainous areas.

11 THE NATURE OF THE TYPICAL
MOUNTAIN-WALLED PLAINS

For more than a century the various craterlike formations of the moon have been classified as mountain-walled plains, ringed plains, crater rings, craters, craterlets, and crater pits. Probably a better classification could be devised today, but new nomenclature would only result in confusion; it seems best to wait until the present disagreement about the nature of these objects has been resolved before changes are made. The traditional names are descriptive and have the merit of implying nothing with regard to origin, about which there is a great deal of speculation. One of the new terms that is sometimes used and is suggestive of type of origin is "endocrater," which would apply to any craterlike formation considered in the context to be the result of causes that were internal—within the moon itself. Even a shallow, local, accidental depression would then be considered as an endocrater.

Conspicuous among those considered here to be endocraters are the mountain-walled plains. Neison describes them as follows:

"Walled plains extend from 40 to 150 miles in diameter, and are seldom surrounded by a single wall, but usually by an intricate system of mountain ranges, separated by valleys, crossed by ravines, and united to one another at various points by cross-walls and buttresses; all usually, however, subordinate to one or two principal ranges, forming a massive crest to the rest. Toward the exterior and interior extend numerous projections and arms, at times rising even above the wall and at others low, short, and insignificant. Occasionally, as on Schiller and Posidonius, these arms extend throughout the greater portion of the interior, or even divide it into two portions. Toward the exterior, these branching arms and projecting buttresses occasionally unite two or more walled-plains together, and at times these rise into considerable ridges, often enclosing long valleys. The interiors of the walled-plains are as a rule comparatively level, sometimes, as in Plato and Archimedes, only broken by a few mounds, or perhaps by a crater cone or so; but more usually the interior is interrupted by a number of small irregularities, as ridges, mounds, or crater pits, as in Maginus and Ptolemy; whilst at times these irregularities assume considerable dimensions, as in Posidonius, Gassendi, and Catharina. Though many are roughly circular in shape, others possess very irregular outlines, appearing more like several confluent plains, or like a space enclosed by intersecting mountain chains rather than as true independent formations.

"Though commonly classed under the crateriform formations of the moon, the true walled-plains would appear to be related rather to the mares or plains, more especially to those mares bordered by great highlands and mountains like the Mares Crisium and Serenitatis, to which certain of the great walled-plains, as Clavius, Maginus, Ptolemaeus, Hipparchus, and Schickhardt, bear a considerable resemblance, though on a smaller scale—a circumstance that did not escape Maedler. A close examination of such examples of the walled-plain as these would suggest their being low-lying bright plains surrounded by mountain ranges and extensive highlands, rather than actual independent formations bearing any relation to true volcanoes, and, as Maedler remarks, had Clavius possessed a dark interior, and been nearer the centre, Riccioli would have probably classed it as a mare, and the same holds good with some of the others."

There are certain data which must be explained, or at the very least not contradicted, by any satisfactory hypothesis concerning the nature of the typical mountain-walled plains. These are:

1. They are very shallow in respect to their diameters.

2. They have low or no external walls.

3. They seldom have central peaks.

4. The walls are not circular, but rather are rectangular, square, and especially hexagonal.

5. Many small craters are found on their rims.

6. The floors tend toward smoothness.

7. They become inconspicuous under a high sun.

8. They have diameters from approximately 50 to 150 miles. The lower limit is inherited, and arbitrary.

9. They are found only in mountainous areas.

10. They resemble those of the maria which are bounded by scarps.

11. Scarps and lines of small craters sometimes are observed along lines which are the mu-

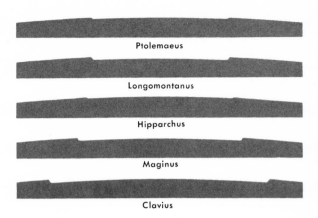

Figure 11. Vertical sections through typical walled plains.

tual extensions of the boundaries of neighboring plains.

12. The walls are not continuous; gaps are common.

13. They have no ray systems.

14. Some—Ptolemaeus (Plate 11–2) is the best example—have numerous "ghosts" on their floors.

15. In general, if a piece of paper is laid over a photograph so that it just touches the inner edge of the boundary scarp, there is nothing visible to indicate that any unusual depression has been covered.

The accompanying diagram attempts to show vertical sections of several of the largest walled plains on a true scale. Heights of the ridges are not known accurately and it is probable that the average heights are even less than those used in the diagram. This statement applies especially to Longomontanus, for which the old measurements appear to be clearly excessive. Usually the wall contains some mountains much higher than the average. Often gaps occur in the walls. Plate 9–1, showing Ptolemaeus at sunset, exhibits both of these features.

Some lunar features conform to most of the characteristics of mountain-walled plains but differ more or less widely from the typical examples. In some cases the differences are so great that one may wonder whether the object should not be more properly classified as a ringed plain. Perhaps a category for this kind of hybrid should be created, intermediate to the classical divisions. Such intermediate examples show evidence

Plate 11–1. Mt. Wilson and Palomar Observatories, 1954 May 24ᵈ 11ʰ 36ᵐ UT, phase 21.63 days, colongitude 172°. Kodak IIa–O plate, no filter. The Ptolemaeus area near sunset.

Plate 11–2. Mt. Wilson and Palomar Observatories, 1956 October 26ᵈ 12ʰ 56ᵐ UT, phase 22.35 days, colongitude 177°. Detail of floor of Ptolemaeus.

of more or less explosive action and they exhibit more than traces of external walls.

The trio seen on Plates 3–19 and 11–1, Ptolemaeus, Alphonsus, and Arzachel, have all been considered to be mountain-walled plains. Ptolemaeus is a typical one. Alphonsus is definitely related to it generically and does exhibit the hexagonal wall. However, there is also evidence of explosive action in the formation of Alphonsus, and there is a noticeable external wall. It would appear to be probable that the explosive action came late in its formation. Arzachel appears also to have been initiated by collapse, but the later explosive action was so violent that there could be no objection to classifying it as an explosive ringed plain.

In judging the existence of an external wall, care must be exercised lest a contiguous feature prove deceptive. If a mare is nearby, for instance,

the slope to its surface may create a false impression of a wall. A large depressed area, such as the one bounded by Arzachel, Alphonsus, Ptolemaeus, Albategnius, and smaller features to the south on Plate 3–19 may produce such an illusion. Plato on Plate 10–19 is listed as a walled plain by both Neison and Goodacre. Possibly it is, but if so it was much altered by the formation of Mare Imbrium. It is located on the narrow island of ground that separates Maria Imbrium and Serenitatis from Frigoris. The slopes to these maria, which were formed later, may possibly have produced a fictitious external wall. Archimedes, on the same plate, is a ringed plain, and is so listed by Goodacre despite Neison's erroneous classification.

In contrast to those craterlike formations that have considerable external slopes, there is little tendency for the typical walled plains to 109 be circular. By way of example, Plates 11–1, and 11–2 and 3–19 show Ptolemaeus as an almost perfect hexagon. Albategnius, another hexagon, lies to the left of it. Hipparchus, just north of Albategnius, has almost lost its lower right wall, but the remaining southern boundary of the plain is more nearly part of a square than anything else. The boundary wall of Hipparchus is nearly as low as is that of Deslandres, and even while the sun still is moderately low (Plate 4–7) it becomes difficult to find. Directly right of the southern side of Ptolemaeus is a small unnamed plain (Plate 11–1), which is nearly a perfect rectangle.

Farther south (Plates 3–19 and 8–1) is the sequence Purbach, Regiomontanus, and Walter. Regiomontanus is a rather good square, except for the fact that Purbach has cut off its lower right hand corner. Walter also shows somewhat the same tendency. To the right of these is the

Plate 11–3. Clavius corrected for foreshortening (see Appendix).

very large and very shallow old plain, Deslandres. It also roughly approximates a square. It appears that the largest of the mountain-walled plains are the oldest and perhaps the most typical ones. Deslandres is so old that several later features have formed on it. It also is so shallow that it was not listed by the early observers. However, when the sun is very low (Plates 13–1 and 13–2) it is revealed as one of the finest lunar depressions. Similarly Janssen (Plates 15–2 and 15–5) is easy to miss, except when the sun is quite low, because of both its low walls and the many later features that camouflage it.

Clavius, the second largest of the typical walled plains, is found near the top of Plate 8–5. Almost at a glance one observes the many craters at and near the rim, the lack of external wall, the general smoothness of the floor, and the beautiful arc of craters on that floor, starting with Rutherford on the southern wall. The true form of Clavius is difficult to distinguish because it is near the southern limb of the moon. However, the floor is observable as a somewhat irregular polygon, marred by the more recent Rutherford in one corner. This is revealed clearly by Plate 11–3 in which the area near Clavius is corrected for foreshortening; see page 182 of the appendix. Close examination reveals that there is something peculiar about the southern side. The southern part of the floor is seen to extend southward at a higher level, as a pass between extensions of the walls. The right extension becomes an outer left wall for Blancanus and the left extension serves as an outer right hand wall for Gruemberger. Each of these is a walled plain more than 50 miles in diameter. This pass is probably one example of very old surface features that have become almost fully camouflaged. It is related to a much larger and very old depression just to the left of Clavius. Clavius apparently was formed in its right hand section. When the lighting is sufficiently low the wall of the large depression can be glimpsed running to the upper left from a point just north of Clavius. As seen in Plate 8–5, the depression next makes a turn to the upper right and passes barely south of Gruemberger. This slightly depressed area may be the oldest feature observable on the moon today.

Grimaldi, near the right limb, is one of the largest of the walled plains. Foreshortening disguises its form, but the globe projection method

Plate 11–4. The Copernicus-Kepler-Olbers-Seleucus-Aristarchus oversystem of rays, partially corrected for foreshortening (see Appendix).

(Plate 11–4) shows it in nearly its true shape. It is revealed as a hexagon with a mutilated northern wall where a pass leads to Oceanus Procellarum. Grimaldi is morphologically truly a connecting link between the maria and the typical walled plains. On its shoreline on the right can be seen the remains of several craters whose "seaward" walls sank during the formation of Grimaldi.

If the walled plains were due primarily to explosions, either internal or external, we would not expect to find these polygons. But we might well expect them if the typical walled plains were in fact somewhat similar to what geologists call calderas: craters formed by collapse, often along a fault line. (The walled plain Schiller re-

sembles a terrestrial "graben," a sunken area between faults.)

The evidence favoring a caldera-like explanation of the walled plains is emphasized by a study of the lines along which the sides lie. In Plate 11–1 examination of the northern wall of Ptolemaeus shows that it contains a line of small craters. As the line of craters is extended to the left from Ptolemaeus it merges with the northern wall of Albategnius. The coincidence is too great to accept as accidental. This is perhaps the most striking example of this kind of linear relationship between large neighboring walled plains that are not in actual contact.

As another example, the left wall of Walter can be observed, on Plate 8–1, continuing south-

111

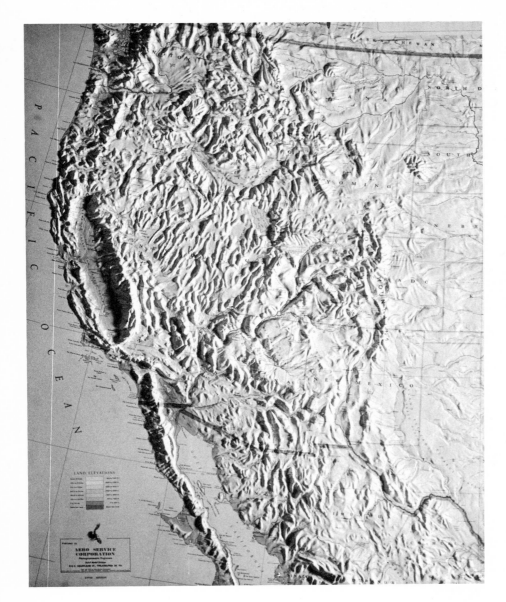

Plate 11–5. The great mountain-walled plain in California. (Courtesy of Aero Science Corporation.)

ward in a conspicuous manner beyond the floor for a distance equal to the diameter of the plain, and can be picked up at intervals for a much greater distance southward. Under the morning lighting of this plate Walter appears like the heel of a giant's footprint.

Plate 8–5 shows a large area of the rough section of the moon south of Mare Nubium. In it there are several places where the rim of a craterlike formation continues conspicuously beyond the depressed area, either as a scarp or as a row of craters.

The small craters at or close to the rims of these plains are too numerous, as compared with the numbers in the surrounding areas, to be accidental. This fact may be easily observed by examination of Plate 8–5. Clavius, the second largest of the walled plains, exhibits these small craters. To the right of Clavius, Scheiner has a nice ring of them. Below and slightly to the left of Clavius, Maginus shows perhaps more of them than any other plain. Directly across from Maginus, Longomontanus shows a similar formation. North of Longomontanus, Wilhelm I has a rather delicate ring of small craters. Near the bottom of the picture, the partially ruined Pitatus continues the story. This excess of small craters quite definitely indicates weaknesses in the rock at these places. In many cases lines of these craters appear to resemble somewhat our terrestrial blowhole craters. Observed strings of them doubtless lie along fractures of the rock.

These data indicate strongly that typical mountain-walled plains, examples of which are listed below, are not due primarily to explosions either from internal or from external causes. The numbers following the names are the (x, y) coordinates from the map of Plates 3–1 and 3–2.

Albategnius (66, 84)	Maginus (72, 119)
Clavius (75, 124)	Ptolemaeus (74, 82)
Deslandres (74, 106)	Purbach (72, 99)
Hipparchus (65, 78)	Scheiner (80, 124)
Janssen (38, 114)	Walter (70, 106)
Longomontanus (84, 118)	Wilhelm I (85, 114)

In searching for the cause of these objects one may be tempted to accept the hypothesis of the collapse of great domes. Small domes, and craterlets that have resulted from the collapse of large domes, have definitely been found on the moon. Great domes have been postulated on the earth. Their terrestrial existence, however, is controversial, except perhaps for a few instances. For example, the central plain of California has been cited as being the result of dome collapse, but instead almost surely it was caused by the tipping of the Sierra block. This great terrestrial "mountain-walled plain" is shown by Plate 11–5, in which the height of the boundary wall is exaggerated. If large domes ever existed on the moon they were formed by great upward fluid pressure beneath the surface. Such a pressure might have been gaseous in nature, or the result of steam from rock-locked water in the interior. A more likely guess as to the agent would be expansion and fluid rock resulting from changes of phase of some of the minerals in the lunar mantle. The collapse of such domes could be due to fracturing of the surface rock as they were lifted too high, or to triggering impacts by meteorites. Meteoritic impact cannot, however, account for the form in which we now see the great mountain-walled plains. At present the dome hypothesis of the origin of these objects cannot be entirely rejected, but it does seem

improbable. The areas appear to be too small for lack of isostasy to serve as a satisfactory hypothesis for their origin (although this may be possible in the case of the largest maria). Perhaps, after all, not all these features had the same kind of origin. Whereas some of them may actually be related to the maria genetically, others may merely have a superficial morphological resemblance. Certainly the origins of the craterlike formations (ringed plains) that exhibit considerable external slopes must be different from those of the mountain-walled plains. For the former some type or types of explosions are indicated.

A last word on the caldera hypothesis: it is of course dangerous to argue from morphological resemblances between features on the moon and on the earth, which is much greater in mass and possesses an atmosphere. It would be equally wrong to neglect such features completely. Plate 11–6 is an aerial photograph of an active caldera in the Galapagos Islands. The picture was made by the U.S. Air Force in cooperation with the Ecuadorian government and supplied through the courtesy of Dr. Jack Green, a geologist who is making a special study of calderas.

The resemblance of such terrestrial calderas to mountain-walled plains such as Ptolemaeus, Grimaldi, Clavius, and the large old plain that includes the Straight Wall must not be ignored. The same holds for ringed plains such as Eratosthenes, Theophilus, and Archimedes, and for the Maria Crisium and Serenitatis, even including their continental shelves.

There is need for a great deal more research. At this stage these judgments concerning mountain-walled plains appear to be justified:

1. Some of them are closely related in nature to the maria.

2. If any explosions occurred in their formation, they were at most merely triggerlike ones.

3. They are large sunken surfaces in mountainous areas of the moon, and are usually of polygonal form.

4. They often show specific relationships to neighboring features.

5. Small craters at or near their rims indicate that there has been sinking along fault lines.

6. Some of them appear to be the oldest features observable on the moon today.

7. Probably most are some form of caldera. 113

Plate 11–6. Active caldera in the Galapagos. (U.S. Air Force
in cooperation with the Ecuadorian Government.)

12 THE EXPLOSION CRATERS

The evidence offered by the surface of the moon indicates that in general its evolution was comparatively quiet; most of the surface features are simply not of a kind that indicates very violent explosions. The maria appear largely to have been the results of subsidence and outflow; there is little or no reason to believe that explosions were a significant factor in their evolution except in the central part of Mare Imbrium, Plate 10–22. The same appears to be true of the next largest class of features, the typical mountain-walled plains, which have maximum diameters exceeding 150 miles.

However, large and violent explosions have taken place. The two best known of these are discussed descriptively in Chapters 7 and 8. At full moon phase a person viewing the scene can almost imagine the explosions to be occurring now. Eleven of the principal examples of such violent explosions are marked on the accompanying plate, keyed by number to the list below it. The numbers in parentheses are the brightnesses as stated by Neison; see Chapter 2.

Any satisfactory hypothesis concerning explosion craters (both the ringed plains and the smaller craters) must explain, or at least not contradict, the following facts:

1. The explosion craters have definite external walls.

2. Many of the explosion craters brighten much more than do the neighboring features under a high sun.

3. Others, such as Eratosthenes (Plates 7–1—7–5) almost disappear when shadows are short.

4. The inner walls of some of the larger craters, such as Copernicus, have terraces.

5. Craterlets are commonly found around the rims of all except the smallest craters.

6. Unlike the typical mountain-walled plains, which are found only in mountainous areas, explosion craters exist in all kinds of terrain.

7. Lines of craterlets exist on the outer walls and in the neighboring areas of some of the explosion craters. This is much more conspicuous for Copernicus and Tycho than for any of the less violent ringed plains. Sometimes these craterlets coalesce to form rills (clefts); see Plates 7–1, 7–2, and 8–7. Usually the rills tend to be radial to the primary explosion but some rills point in other directions or even follow curved loci.

8. Some of the outer slopes of explosion craters exhibit valleys that give at least a casual impression of having been formed by erosion. Aristillus (Plate 10–19) is an excellent example.

115

Plate 12–1. Ringed plains of apparently unusually violent origins. See Plate 5–2 for technical details.

1. Anaxagoras (7)
2. Aristarchus (8–10)
3. Byrgius (6–7, crater 8)
4. Copernicus (9)
5. Kepler (7)
6. Manilius (8)
7. Menelaus (8–9)
8. Olbers (6)
9. Proclus (8–9)
10. Thales (6–8)
11. Tycho (8 crest)

9. Central mountains or groups of hills are common within these craters, whereas they are rather rare within the typical mountain-walled plains.

10. Most, although not all, explosion craters exhibit a tendency toward circularity. This contrasts strongly with the rims of the mountain-walled plains which show a definite tendency toward polygonal shape.

11. Perhaps each of those craters which brighten definitely under a high sun shows at least one ray (bright streak) which belongs to it. In some cases such as Tycho, Copernicus, and the starlike craterlets on the outer slopes of Furnerius and Stevinus, the ray systems are large and complicated. It is possible that systems of faint rays belong to some craters which do not brighten much. Mountain-walled plains do not have ray systems.

Some craterlets, such as those on the rims to the right of the walled plains Furnerius and Stevinus (Plates 3–4 and 4–9), also indicate tremendous, although highly localized, explo-

sions. Near full moon the bright craters and their rays are as conspicuous as are the maria and the great mountainous areas. The violence of their explosions is attested to not only by the changed albedo over large areas but also by the ray systems and in some cases by the numerous craterlets in the neighborhood. Still, the total area of all these violent features is only a small fraction of even the mountainous areas in general.

The ray systems prove that at least some of these explosions were among comparatively recent catastrophic events. Nevertheless, the mare-like areas right of Tycho cannot have subsided much earlier than the time that Tycho (Plate 10–4) was formed. If they were formed before Tycho they had not yet cooled sufficiently to permit Tycho's major rays to cross the area. Tycho's lower right rim (Plate 8–6) is slightly cut by an oval partial depression, which must have been formed more recently than Tycho. Palus Somnii to the right of Proclus (Plate 10–12) cannot have antedated Proclus, although the subsidence may have occurred at the same time as the explosion.

The evidence of extreme violence in all these cases is so great that one must agree with Gilbert, Baldwin, Urey, Kuiper, and others that, at least initially, these craters were formed by meteoritic or asteroidal impacts. No other hypothesis seems adequate to account for the tremendous release of energy on the rather quiet moon. The small, starlike craterlets, which dot the surface of the full moon, may be assumed to be entirely the results of meteoritic impact.

But at least in the cases of Tycho and Copernicus, the numerous craters that have formed in their vicinities testify to the probability that subsequent volcanic action took place on a large scale. This evidence is strengthened by the easily observable terraces on their inner walls, which indicate subsequent collapsing that increased the craters' diameters. The hypothesis of subsequent volcanic action is almost demanded, moreover, by the presence of craterlets on the rims, indicating faults along which subsidence occurred.

The arc of craterlets on the left hand floor of Tycho surely must be volcanic. This volcanism may be merely an indirect result of the impact explosion, but it does exist. Tycho, Copernicus, and probably other large craters of this class, then, must be of a composite nature: impact-volcanic.

In contrast to the very bright craters, which clearly are, at least in part, of impact origin, there is a second class of large explosion craters that show little or no difference either of shade or color from the surrounding areas, regardless of the height of the sun. The external walls indicate that explosions did occur, but it appears probable that the explosions may have been much less violent than those connected with impact craters of equal size. In general these second-rank explosion craters do not exhibit ray systems or an unusual density of nearby craterlets. Eratosthenes, which may be an immense mountain with a large crater at its summit, is perhaps the best example. Quite possibly the top of the mountain collapsed into a partially hol-

Plate 12–2. Large ringed plains of apparently moderately violent origin. See Plate 5–2 for technical details.

1. Aliacensis
2. Aristillus (4–4½)
3. Arzachel (4)
4. Atlas (5)
5. Autolycus (3–5)
6. Cassini (4)
7. Cyrillus (4, crater 7)
8. Eratosthenes (3½–4)
9. Hercules (5, crater 8–9)
10. Lambert (4)
11. Theophilus (5)

Plate 12–3. Mt. Wilson and Palomar Observatories, 1955 October 8^{d} 12^{h} 48^{m}
UT, phase 22.27 days, colongitude 176°. Detail of the Apennines.

low interior after either an ejection of the mountain building material or a recession. If this be true, Eratosthenes, in its present condition, is a magnificent caldera. Its albedo is almost the same within the crater, at the rim, and on the mountain wall. The crater and its mountain disappear as completely at noon as do the typical mountain-walled plains. Plates 7–1 through 7–3 exhibit this characteristic difference between the two classes of ringed plains.

However, one must not be dogmatic concerning the hypothesis that the violence of an explosion caused the main differences between the two types of ringed plains. Craters which lack ray systems and excessive noonday brightening may merely be older. According to this hypothesis meteoritic or other dust has covered the rays and the craters. This result appears certain if there was sufficient difference in age. The author inclines strongly to the former hypothesis but he realizes that the truth may not be known until long after man has begun his explorations on the moon.

The positions of some of the largest, non-brightening ringed plains are marked on the accompanying photograph (Plate 12–2) of the full moon. Arzachel and Cyrillus are hybrids and possibly should have been omitted. Neison did not give the brightness of Aliacensis. The brightnesses of these craters compare with the general level of the bright mountainous areas, an average between 4 and 5, whereas the first list averages more than 7.

There are other craters which appear at first glance to be rather bright merely because they are located on the dark floors of maria.

It is difficult to classify some of the ringed plains with respect to brightness. The rings themselves are not especially bright, but each is associated with an intensely bright craterlet. The string of rather large rings extending southward from Abulfeda is notable for this characteristic. Abulfeda (4½, peak 7) has a bright central peak whose relationship to the ring appears not to be accidental. The next in line, Almanon (5½, craterlet 8+), has rather similar characteristics with a small, bright craterlet on its outer wall. The third of the string is Abenezra (5, craterlet 6), which is lost at full moon except for the bright craterlet to the right of it. Apianus (craterlet 8 on the left wall) follows with a very

bright craterlet. These are four members of an arc of seven large ringed plains (Plate 3–8) which form the left boundary of a tremendous, slightly depressed area that is bounded on the right by one of the great lunar scarps. The craterlets indicate at least trigger action in formation of the craters but the unusual alignment seems to contradict such a hypothesis. The best guess is that the rings do lie along a complex, perhaps Tychonian, fault which provided preferential conditions for the action of large meteorites. If this be true the seven are, for the main part, endocraters.

The best photographs show too many small craters concentrated in the mountainous areas bordering Sinus Iridum, in the Alps, the Caucasus, and the Apennines to be accidental. Plate 12–3 is an enlargement of the Apennine area. Some of the craters there are deep, while others are very shallow and may be merely accidental depressions. Shown on this plate, in addition to craters, are a number of domes. These craters are small for the most part. It appears probable that most of the deeper examples are endocraters, resembling the terrestrial volcanic craters more closely than do any other lunar features.

The available evidence concerning non-brightening lunar craters does not distinguish with certainty in individual cases between impact and endo-lunar origin. Those features of this kind that are due to impact would seem to have been caused by meteorites or asteroids striking the lunar surface at far lower velocities than was the case in the great explosions. Of course, we must remember the possibility of dimming with age. The distribution of these craters favors an endo-lunar origin for most of them. Except for those marked by bright craterlets, almost none of these non-brightening, rather large craters with high external walls are found in mountainous regions, far from maria. Nearly all of them are either in or close to maria. In other words, they are found in the regions that provide the greatest evidence of flows of molten rock. Perhaps their relationship to the maria is somewhat similar to that of Copernicus and Tycho to their surrounding craterlets.

It would appear reasonable also that some of the craters that brighten only moderately under a high sun are endocraters for which the explosive forces were unusually large. Lines of such craters, as, for example, the moderately bright examples along the great ray to the left from Tycho to Mare Nectaris, appear to demand an origin other than direct impact.

The fact that such large volcanic craters are not found on the earth has no weight, either pro or con. We do not find craters like Copernicus here either. Surely great impact explosions must have occurred on the earth if they did on the moon, but the resulting very large craters would have been eroded by our atmosphere. It is possible, on the other hand, that no large explosive craters, either of the endocrater or the impact variety, may ever have existed on the earth. Crater-forming forces are comparatively localized and the moon is large enough that mere size does not preclude explosive forces there from equaling the terrestrial forces. On the earth an explosive force would have worked against six times the weight of similar masses on the moon, and tremendous craters may simply not have been produced.

The distribution of the largest of the violent explosion craters has led to an interesting and suggestive observation. It has been noted that these features tend to group themselves in the north preceding part of the moon. The diameter drawn on the accompanying Plate 12–1 shows that ten of the eleven greatest explosions belong to one hemisphere. Such a number is too small to do more than indicate a good possibility that the grouping is not accidental. But the chance of non-accidental grouping of these features is increased by the fact that during all the eons of time that the moon has kept one face toward the earth, the right limb is the one that has been the "leading edge" in its orbit around the earth. A very tentative guess toward an explanation, then, is that asteroids belonging to the earth-moon system, rather than to the sun, have played a very important part in the evolution of the lunar surface and have inevitably made their mark more conspicuously upon the exposed right limb, which has always faced them directly. The observed phenomenon of hemispheric concentration would have to be laid to chance only if these ringed plains were the results of impacts by solar asteroids. Despite the apparent logic of this explanation, the truth of the matter may eventually prove to be very different.

One other peculiarity that has been observed

is probably due entirely to chance. It may be worth mentioning, however, because data learned at a later time sometimes establish a cause and take the peculiarity from the field of chance. There is a great peninsula of bright, rough ground near the center of the visible disk. It is conspicuous on any photograph of the full moon (Plates 12–1 and 5–2). This peninsula breaks up what would otherwise be a tremendous mare covering most of the central part of our side of the moon. The boundary between the two hemispheres which have been considered in the preceding paragraph is, insofar as can be determined, perpendicular to the axis of the peninsula, and must lie along the slope gradient between Mare Nubium at the right of the peninsula and Mare Tranquillitatis at the left. In general it is approximately perpendicular to the "gashes" which are numerous in the area; see Chapter 15.

One more peculiarity between these preceding and following hemispheres of the moon must be recorded. The total mare area in the right half of the visible disk is several times that in the left, and is particularly large on the lower right side of the diameter discussed above.

The following conclusions concerning explosion craters appear to be justified:

1. The largest craters, which brighten under a high sun, were probably initially meteoritic or asteroidal in origin, but assumed their present form after subsequent endo-lunar action.

2. The small craters that brighten to starlike brilliance were formed by meteoritic impact.

3. Quite a number of non-brightening craters that exhibit bright craterlets are endocraters initiated by meteoritic triggering shocks.

4. The large non-brightening explosion craters are probably in many cases endocraters of the caldera type, although it is at present impossible to be certain in any specific case. The possible dimming with age due to covering by meteoritic dust must be remembered continually.

5. The craters found on the highlands of Sinus Iridum, on the Alps, the Caucasus, and the Apennines probably are mostly endocraters.

6. There is a definite concentration of the principal explosion craters and of the maria in the portion of the moon that constitutes the leading limb as the satellite moves in its orbit through space.

13 THE NATURE OF THE DOMES AND
SMALL CRATERS OF THE MOON

The small craters of the moon are classified by Neison as craterlets, crater pits, and crater cones. All of these categories will be referred to here as small craters or craterlets, although certain characteristics could be used to divide them into subclasses. They vary in size from the smallest observable object of this kind up to about five miles in diameter. The largest ones merge indistinguishably with the larger craters. Domes are similar in appearance to some of the small craters, except that no more than a tiny pit is observable in the top of these low, rounded hills that look something like human skin blisters (see Plate 7–2). The term endocrater will be applied, as in earlier chapters, to any craterlet due to any sort of internal pressure or explosion. This terminology is followed even when the fundamental but indirect cause may have been a nearby, great impact explosion like the one that produced Copernicus.

Any hypothesis concerning the formation of craterlets and domes must explain, or at least not contradict, the following data:

1. Many and perhaps all of the craterlets have external walls.

2. Lines of craterlets are common. Sometimes the lines are curved and form complex patterns. The craterlets in these lines do not brighten to a starlike appearance under a high sun.

3. Some of the lines are composed of both craterlets and domes.

4. Isolated craterlets are common on the mare floors. They generally appear to have floors deeper than the surrounding mare.

5. The typical isolated mare-floor craterlets have the same general appearance as the domes, except that the former have an opening in the top. These craterlets rather resemble collapsed domes.

6. Small craters are common around the rims of large craters and mountain-walled plains.

7. More than a thousand craterlets exist in

the Copernican area and at least hundreds near Tycho.

8. Some of the craterlets brighten very much under a high sun and become starlike. This is the same phenomenon observed in the cases of Tycho, Copernicus, and some others of the larger craterlike formations. Many craterlets brighten moderately. But still others tend to disappear entirely near noon.

9. Many of the craterlets that brighten have tiny ray systems. W. H. Pickering believed that all craterlets that become starlike have this characteristic. Probably he was right.

10. Sometimes elementary rays from craterlets combine to form the complex principal rays of such craters as Tycho and Copernicus.

11. In some cases lines of craterlets have coalesced to form valleys. Careful examination with large instruments reveals signs of craterlets in many—perhaps in the majority—of the rills or clefts. Rheita Valley is the result of such coalescence of larger craters.

Plate 13–1. Features of Deslandres outlined for use as a map. See Plate 8–5 for technical details.

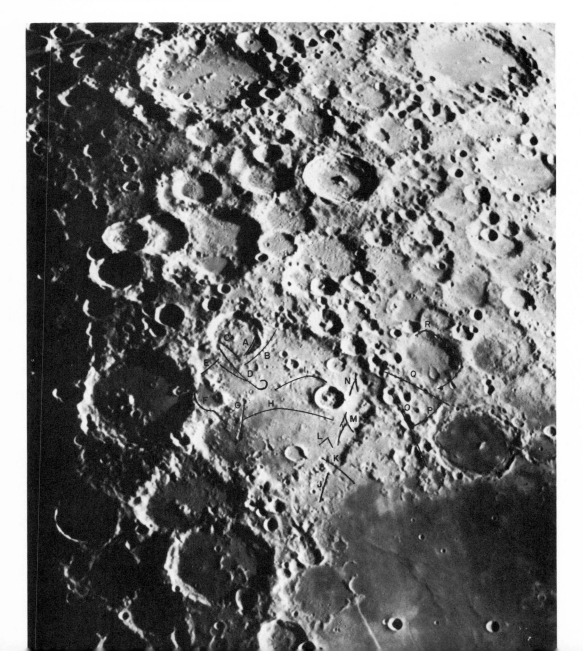

12. Sometimes even fairly large craters form a line. A beautiful example is the north-south line that touches the left hand wall of Pitatus (see Plates 13–1 and 13–2).

13. An arc of craterlets may enclose a partially sunken area. Excellent examples can be found (Plates 13–1 and 13–2) south of Hell and in the lower left hand portion of Lexell.

14. Many small craters can be observed on the Apennines (Plate 12–3) under favorable conditions. Somewhat larger ones are observable on the highlands of Sinus Iridum. The Alps and the Caucasus also show such craterlets.

Craterlets will be discussed here under the following four classifications:

1. Craterlets near large explosion craters; 2. craterlets on or near rims and floors of craterlike formations; 3. lines of craterlets and domes; 4. craterlets that become starlike under a high sun.

1. Plate 7–1 shows the region left of the great explosion crater Copernicus under a very low sun. Eratosthenes is at the lower left of the picture. The ghost ring, Stadius, is below the center. There are hundreds of craterlets forming all sorts of patterns. Even Stadius is, in part, a circle of craterlets. In some places craterlets coalesce to form rills, or narrow valleys. Some of these valleys are radial to Copernicus, but others follow other directions in various ways.

Two ovals of craterlets touch Stadius at a common point on the south, with the smaller oval inside the larger. Under the very low morning sun of this picture the Copernican rays are faint. However, an examination of Plate 7–5 reveals that two oval rays shown there coincide with these oval loci of craterlets. Clearly there is a close relationship between craterlets and the components of major rays—at least on the basis of this evidence.

A little to the left of Copernicus and considerably south of the center of Plate 7–1 is a craterlet of the type common on the floors of the maria. To the left of it is a dome. Just to the south of this crater and dome and extending on the right to an area directly south of Copernicus is one of the three large, rough, dark regions associated with Copernicus and almost unique on the lunar surface. The picture shows about a dozen domes in it. A number of craterlets and small domes can be seen among the hills of the far southern area of the picture. Such domes are too low to be observed when the sun is high above the horizon.

Plate 7–5, extending to the right of Copernicus, does not show as great a mass of craterlets as are visible on the other side, except to the lower right, where they tend to form radial valleys. A beautiful group of five domes is just to the lower left of Hortensius in Plate 7–2. An excellent single dome is shown right of Milichius, and two large, low domes are seen a little farther north of it. There are two tiny pits in the larger of the pair. Several other of these larger domes as well as numerous smaller ones can be seen on the plate.

2. Plate 8–7 was made to exhibit details of Tycho and of the floors of the nearby walled plains. The many craterlets on the flattish floors of mountain-walled plains to the lower left of Tycho tend to form rills radial to that crater. These craterlets are for the most part smaller than those left of Copernicus and there are fewer non-radial rills. On the lower left part of the floor of Tycho is a beautifully curved chain of craterlets approximately parallel to the edge of the floor. To the lower right of Tycho can be seen a large, somewhat sunken oval region composed of small craters, most of which are larger than craterlets. This area breaks the rim of Tycho, and has the distinct appearance of a sinking area that stopped subsiding too soon to be listed as a walled plain. It certainly is newer than Tycho. Rim craterlets may be noted on Tycho as on all large craters.

3. Plate 10–2 shows among other things the Straight Wall, the old walled plain within which it lies, a rill which formed along a line of craterlets right of the wall, and a line of craterlets and domes perpendicular to the wall and reaching it from the left, better seen on Plate 10–3. Such mixed lines of craterlets and domes are important in an interpretation of their nature. The irregular spots in the wall and the craterlets at its ends should be noted.

Important features have been outlined on Plate 13–1 to make possible its use as a map for Plate 13–2. On the lower right hand floor of Lexell is a partly coalesced line of craterlets designated as A. The lines C and D border a valley that extends from the interior of Lexell to

Plate 13–2. The unusual detail in and near Deslandres (see Plate 13–1).
See Plate 8–5 for technical details.

the lower right to "Cassini's Bright Spot." *H* is a long arc composed of both domes and craterlets. Several groups of domes can be observed north of it with a few craterlets mixed in. The line *I* is an arc of craterlets partially surrounding an area that has sunk below the general surface. *O* is a line of craters somewhat larger than craterlets. The crater lines *O-P-Q* bound a triangular area just to upper left of Pitatus. Numerous other lines of craters exist in the area.

Plate 10–21 is a section of the floor of Mare Imbrium, directly south of Promontory Laplace and adjoining the terminator, which is at the extreme left. (See Plate 10–20 for identification of the area.) Under a very low sun the typical mare-type isolated craterlets exhibit their external walls and have at least the appearance of being rounded.

4. Any good photograph taken near full moon (Plate 5–2) will exhibit some of the random craterlets that brighten to starlike appearance under a high sun. They appear to be the results of explosions too violent to have originated on the same rather quiet moon that produced the maria and mountain-walled plains, and it seems best to attribute their origin to meteoritic impact. Others, which brighten to a lesser degree, may result in some cases from impact but in other cases may be the product of unusually violent endo-explosions. There is, however, a small cloud on the horizon insofar as this line of reasoning is concerned: If all starlike craterlets are meteoritic, why do the adjacent hybrid walled plains Furnerius and Stevinus (Plates 5–2 and 14–2) both show in their right hand walls two of the very brightest of all craterlets? As a mere guess, perhaps two meteorites struck in an area where existing faults, complicated by some extended volcanic action, made conditions favorable for surface collapse. The impact may have supplied the trigger to produce the larger features. On the other hand, perhaps this association of bright craterlets and walled plains is merely accidental. This whole area from Mare Australis right to Mare Nectaris is a strange one with scarps and small sunken areas abounding (Plates 15–2 and 15–5).

At first thought another difficulty would appear to exist, arising from the fact that so many bright craters are found along Tycho's major rays, especially the one extending on the left to Mare Nectaris (Plate 8–4). It would be difficult to accept this line as due to impact craters. However, the nature of complex rays indicates that the rays appeared where they did because craters had formed there along fault loci that had been enlarged by the Tycho explosion. It is reasonable to assume that such endocraters might be more violent than the ordinary ones of their class, and therefore modified the ground to a greater extent. They do not reach starlike brightness.

The following conclusions concerning craterlets and domes appear to be warranted:

1. Volcanic craterlets near the great explosion craters appear, for the most part, to be a result of those explosions, even though the original explosions that formed the large craters may have been due to impact. Shoemaker and others consider such craters to be due to impact.

2. In many cases such craterlets must have formed along faults.

3. The craterlets near the rims of large craters and mountain-walled plains are volcanic and indicate faults in the surface rock.

4. Mixed lines of craterlets and domes exist, indicating a common generic nature.

5. Possibly the domes are bubbles formed by internal gas (conceivably including steam) pressure. Or a tube of molten rock may have elevated the surface locally, especially in connection with phase changes of minerals in the lunar mantle.

6. Most of the isolated small craters on the mare floors are endocraters.

7. Probably the typical rounded, isolated craterlet of the mare floors is the result of the collapse or bursting of domes. The domes look like the mounds that form on the surface of a gently boiling pot of corn-meal mush; the isolated mare craterlets look like the remains of such collapsed "mush domes."

8. The origin of the isolated craters that become starlike under a high sun is probably meteoritic impact.

9. Some of the isolated craterlets that merely brighten moderately are probably due to low-velocity meteoritic impacts. Others of this kind are very probably endocraters. Not enough data are available to establish definite criteria for individual craterlets of this type.

10. Many rills, or clefts, exhibit endocraterlets.

125

14 THE NATURE OF THE LUNAR RAYS

Much of the interpretation of lunar features is controversial, but nothing is more so than the rays and the ray systems. Under a low sun they become inconspicuous, but at full moon they demand attention from even the most casual observer.

The following data are generally accepted by students of the rays:

1. There is very strong tendency for ray systems to be conspicuous only under a high sun.

2. The systems of bright rays are related to crater-like features that brighten under a high sun in a manner similar to that of the rays themselves.

3. In major systems short, "plume"-shaped rays are common, usually with their axes radial to the parent crater.

4. The long, major rays are complex and usually are not exactly radial.

5. Conspicuous ray systems are not necessarily related to ·large craters.

6. Many short, plume-like single rays issue from bright craterlets or at least from bright spots.

7. Often, perhaps always, the rays appear to be some sort of surface marking, although they may lie along scarps and ridges.

8. A ray appears at close to the same co-longitude each month.

9. Rays are observable in all types of topography. However, a bright, rough surface makes their observation more difficult for observers on earth.

The hypotheses concerning the nature of the rays fall into two general groups:

1. The rays consist of, or at least result directly from, ejecta expelled by the parent craters.

2. The rays are due to gaseous material or to dust that issued from craterlets or from faults in the ray area. These craterlets and faults are related to the primary crater.

At present some form of ejecta hypothesis is favored by the majority of lunar students who are trained in physical theory.

Five diagrams have been included in this chapter as aids in identifying features of the rays. The 108 features numbered on the diagrams were traced from the photographs to which each diagram is keyed. The numbers in parentheses, following the names of these features in the general discussion, refer to the list. The alphabetical list of the features follows:

Table 5

1	Abenezra	55	Landsberg
2	Abulfeda	56	Lindenau
3	Agrippa	57	Marius
4	Albategnius	58	Maurolycus
5	Almanon	59	Menelaus
6	Alphonsus	60	Milichius
7	Archimedes	61	Mösting
8	Aristarchus	62	Oval, large
9	Azophi	63	Oval, small
10	Bessarion	64	Parry
11	Bessel	65	Piccolomini
12	Biot	66	Pitatus
13	Bonpland	67	Pitiscus
14	Brayley	68	Plato
15	Bulliardus	69	Polybius
16	Byrgius	70	Polybius A
17	"Cassini's Bright Spot"	71	Polybius B
18	Catharina	72	Polybius K
19	Clairaut	73	Pons B
20	Clavius	74	Pons C
21	Copernicus	75	Pons E
22	Copernicus bright spot	76	Posidonius
		77	Proclus
23	Cyrillus	78	Ptolemaeus
24	Darney	79	Pytheas
25	Deslandres	80	Rectangle, unnamed
26	Eratosthenes		
27	Euclides	81	Reichenbach
28	Euler	82	Reinhold
29	Fabricius	83	Rheita
30	Flammarion	84	Rothmann
31	Flamsteed	85	Seleucus
32	Fracastorius	86	Sinus Aestuum
33	Fracastorius E	87	Sinus Iridum
34	Fra Mauro	88	Snellius
35	Furnerius	89	Stadius
36	Furnerius A	90	Stevinus
37	Gambart A	91	Stevinus A
38	Gassendi	92	Stiborius
39	Gay-Lussac	93	Stöfler
40	Geber	94	Tacitus
41	Gemma Frisius	95	Theophilus
42	Godin	96	Timocharis
43	Goodacre	97	Tobias Mayer
44	Guericke	98	Tobias Mayer C
45	Herodotus	99	Triesnecker
46	Herschel	100	Tycho
47	Hind C	101	Vlacq
48	Hortensius	102	Wichmann
49	Janssen	103	Zagut
50	Kaiser C	104	Zagut B
51	Kepler	105	Zagut D
52	Kepler A	106	Zagut L
53	Lalande	107	Zagut P
54	Lambert	108	Zagut R

Plates 14–1 and 14–2 show that a major ray system originates at craterlets just outside and to the right of the hybrid mountain-walled plains Furnerius (35) and Stevinus (90). The first unusual feature of the system is the trapezoid of rays shown quite well on Plate 14–2. On Plates 4–2 and 4–3 the low morning sun reveals the craterlike features but the rays have not yet become visible. On Plate 4–4, at phase 5.35 days, the sun is low enough so the rays do not disguise the general topography. The Stevinus craterlet lies on the longest side of the trapezoid, which begins at Snellius (88) and continues southeastward, touching Rheita (83) and Metius at their left rims. This extended side includes a small, bright crater, in Janssen (49), which has a distinct ray system of its own. At this point it meets the end of one of the great western rays from Tycho (100). Farther south the ray becomes much less distinct but under favorable lighting can be traced to a bright craterlet inside the southern wall of the ringed plain Vlacq (101). Here it appears to end, as does also the least intense of the Tychonian rays to the left.

Another principal ray, apparently from the Furnerius craterlet, ends at Biot (12). The last major ray of the system is long but weak in intensity. It belongs to both the craterlets. It first cuts the northern rim of Reichenbach (81), then enters Mare Nectaris and cuts the northern rim of Fracastorius (32). To the right of Nectaris it cuts the area common to the rims of Theophilus (95) and Cyrillus (23). If the ray is composed of ejecta, these tangencies would appear to be strange. All the rays of the system are conspicuous loci for small craters.

The southernmost of the great rays to the left from Tycho is weak and ordinarily escapes notice, but it can be traced faintly on Plates 5–2 and 14–2, ending indefinitely, with the ray from Stevinus, at the bright craterlet in Vlacq (101). The path of the next of these rays counterclockwise, and its ending on the Stevinus ray at the bright crater in Janssen (49), are definite. Certainly this pattern is not to be expected through chance. The third of these rays is directed toward Stevinus itself. Its origin is at the large mountainwalled plain, Stöfler (93), and it cuts the northern wall of Maurolycus (58).

The most intense of the rays to the left from Tycho exhibits so much evidence concerning the nature of rays, because of both its position and

Plate 14–1. For use, aided by a diagram, in identifying features related to the rays.
See Plate 4–8 for technical details.

its structure, that it is worth describing in detail. Plate 14–1 is chosen to show its position at a low enough sun to permit easy identification of craterlike features. Plate 14–2 provides a normal

Figure 12. Map for Plate 14–1.

view of it as seen just before full moon. Plate 8–4, a day after full moon, was made on an extremely contrasty plate to emphasize certain details of its structure.

For a large part of its length the ray is double, the components separating approximately at the northern rim of Stöfler (93). The southern branch passes just south of the starlike crater Kaiser C (50). That seven-mile-diameter crater has a nice ray system lying within this major ray. Next the ray cuts the southern rim of Gemma Frisius (41). It continues to the left through a bright craterlet and the 18-mile-diameter Zagut B (104) with its smaller flanking craters Zagut P (107) and Zagut D (105). Beyond this it meets bright Zagut R (108) and a very bright unlisted crater. Both of these lie on the northern rim of Zagut (103). Right of Zagut the ray is marked by two bright, small craters, the first of which lies on a pronounced scarp that runs from the Altai Scarp to the lower right rim of Zagut and beyond. Examination of this southern branch on Plate 8–4 shows that it is actually a linear series of bright patches.

The northern branch first attracts attention in the vicinity of Kaiser C (50), which lies between the two branches. It cuts the northern rim of Gemma Frisius (41) but remains much fainter than the southern one, even suffering a long interruption, until it reaches the bright craters Pons B (73) and Pons C (74). Left of these it is almost non-existent until it reaches Pons E (75), 16 miles in diameter, just right of the Altai Scarp. To the left of that scarp it is marked by two craters on a short north-south line: Polybius K (72), which has an extremely bright craterlet on its lower left wall, and Polybius B (71). Following to the left is Polybius A (70), which is ten miles in diameter and possesses a small ray system that lies within the major ray. The last crater to mark the great ray is Fracastorius E (33), nine miles in diameter, on the lower right rim of Fracastorius (32). The ray ends just beyond this at a fainter crater

that marks the junction with the long ray from Stevinus. The Tychonian ray, the one from Stevinus, and a scarp prolonging the outer upper left hand wall of Fracastorius to Piccolomini (65) form a conspicuous "sling" that appears to suspend Fracastorius. The occurrence of these combinations through mere chance, which would necessarily follow from any ejecta hypothesis, would be extremely improbable. Most of the brightness of the great ray results directly from the features that have been described along its path. For an ejecta hypothesis to carry conviction, it should present a reasonable explanation for the initiation of all these craters through ejecta from Tycho. In the area south of the great ray and right of the Stevinus system there is only one bright crater that does not lie on a Tychonian ray. It is Neander N, diameter eight miles, with a beautiful little ray system.

The relationships listed above appear to be reasonable under the following hypothesis: The major explosion that created Tycho shattered

Plate 14–2. Interrelationships of Tycho-Furnerius ray system. See Plate 5–2 for technical details.

Figure 13. Plate 8–4 and map for Plate 8–4. An enlargement of this photograph is in Chapter 8.

the surface rock for a long distance. This produced the nimbus area which, in the case of Tycho, is dark in the inner part and bright in the outer. We see this type of effect quite commonly around the hole drilled by a bullet through a pane of glass. Near the hole there is a nimbus with too much shattering for any pattern to be observable. Beyond this nimbus there is a strong tendency for radial cracks. At the time of the Tycho explosion, many hundreds of small craters formed in and near the nimbus. Gases, escaping from the parent crater, constituted a very low-density outward radial wind and carried the ejected gases and dust from small craters as radial plumes away from them. Such plumes are observed by the hundred, especially in the Copernican area where the original surface was much smoother and darker than that around Tycho.

Wherever there had been previous formation of strong explosion craters, each would have produced, on a smaller scale, the same type of effect as did Tycho, with radial faults extending beyond their small nimbi. Whenever such a minor system had been formed in the vicinity of a still earlier one, the principle of least action would produce a tendency for those of its faults that happened to lie in the direction of the older crater to merge with the latter's faults and reinforce

them. Perhaps the finest example of such cooperation is the Stevinus-Furnerius major ray system. Here two very intense craterlets, reinforced by the perimeter faults of Stevinus and Furnerius and receiving considerable assistance from those of Snellius, Rheita, Fracastorius, Theophilus, Cyrillus, and other pre-existing craters, teamed to form a major system during the pre-Tychonian era. The same type of reinforcement found between neighboring explosion craters would take place when a violent explosion occurred near the extension of a side of a mountain-walled plain. The newly formed system would tend to reinforce the fault containing the side of the older feature. One of the nice examples of such reinforcement is found in the tangencies of the two branches of the intense Tychonian ray with Gemma Frisius (Plates 14–1 and 14–2). A perfect example of fault reinforcement by neighboring craters is the southern branch of this ray. Another is the line in the northern branch beginning with Pons B and ending with Fracastorius E. It appears very difficult to ascribe these five craters directly to ejecta from Tycho; on the other hand it seems plausible that when the overshadowing Tycho explosion occurred, the lesser, pre-existing systems mentioned here modified its effects to produce the effects described above.

Evidence has been presented that pre-existing faults, especially those that are roughly radial to a major explosion, tend to be opened more widely and therefore are apt to be loci for craterlets. In such radial cases the outward plumes can reinforce each other and bring about the formation of a complex major ray. The intensity of the complex ray would be a function of the amount of discharge from the craterlets. Plate 10–1 shows a beautiful example of such a result. A pronounced scarp runs southward from the shore of Mare Nubium starting at a point right of Pitatus. For part of the path near the mare, the scarp is double. It is directed toward the right hand portion of Tycho, near which it divides again to continue as a "V" almost to the rim of Clavius. Under proper low lighting it is fairly easy to trace the whole path. Plate 10–1 was exposed at a phase long enough before sunset so that both the scarp and Tycho's double ray are observable and the rather close coincidence can be noted. The scarp certainly cannot have been formed by ejecta from Tycho. The right hand ray in this region contains an excess of craters of various sizes, which are visible along its path in the mare. The mare section of the fainter left component, however, deserves the

more study. Until it reaches the craters just south of Bullialdus, it consists almost entirely of five brightish streaks. Near the center of the strongest of them is a conspicuous double craterlet. Craterlets exist in two of the others and are easy to visualize in the remaining two. To be sure, the craters could be explained by either of the two ray-formation hypotheses, for one might, with Shoemaker, think of each craterlet as having been formed by an ejectus from Tycho. The ejectum hypothesis, however, must accept pure chance as the reason for the correspondence of the ray with the scarp.

When we examine the Copernicus-Kepler-Aristarchus triangle (Plate 7–6), we find the same strange coincidences which were observed on a larger scale in the Tycho and Stevinus-Furnerius systems. One complication partially masks the relationships: Major rays cannot be observed within the shattered nimbi of great explosive craters. In the Tycho-Stevinus over-system there was a great distance through which we could trace the paths of four connecting rays. In this second example the distance between the nimbi of Copernicus and Kepler is only a third of that between the craters themselves. Although a slight study is possible in

Figure 14. Plate 7–6 and map for Plate 7–6. An enlargement of this photograph is in Chapter 7.

this region, it is only the rays that also involve Aristarchus (8) that give definite evidence concerning interrelationships. The brightest spot (22) on Copernicus is found on its outer right wall. The spot is not listed in the IAU catalogue and is not mentioned by Neison, Goodacre, or Wilkins. At colongitude 38° it appears as a single craterlet, but it is actually complex. To the right, as soon as the badly shattered area has been passed, we observe a complex ray leading directly away from it toward Kepler A (52).

Three major rays lead in the general direction from Copernicus toward Aristarchus. One of them is observed first at Tobias Mayer C (98) or perhaps at the very bright nearby double craterlet Tobias Mayer H. Next it passes through a bright craterlet (perhaps K but not listed in the IAU catalogue) with a small ray system. The ray finally merges with a ray from Aristarchus in the area north of Bessarion (10). The next ray (north) connects Tobias Mayer (97) and Aristarchus. The last of three appears first to the north of Tobias Mayer and extends to Brayley (14) where a ray from Aristarchus takes over.

The rays between Kepler (51) and Aristarchus are the best examples. The two craters are connected directly by two narrow rays, each of which extends the whole distance. Just to the right of this pair a ray from Kepler ends at Marius (57), as does a ray from Aristarchus. When one observes these last rays and lets his eye continue the arc through Euclides (27) to Bullialdus (15) and Tycho, Plate 5–2, he must steel himself to accept the arrangement as mere coincidence! To the right of Aristarchus the same type of coincidences connect these craters to Olbers and Seleucus (85) (Plate 11–4). It should be observed that the strong ray from Seleucus forms the northern boundary of the much disturbed area north of Aristarchus. This becomes natural if the ray follows a great fault. It would be similar to the situation that causes the great ray from Tycho to end at the right hand ray from Stevinus.

Even without the data from the Tycho-Stevinus system, these coincidences suggest that the positions of rays from one crater sometimes affect those from another. However, by themselves the rays of the Copernicus-Kepler-Aristarchus triangle cannot be considered sufficient proof. The coincidences may be due to chance.

When we consider the most elementary detail of the ray systems of Copernicus, Plate 7–5,

Figure 15. Plate 5–2 and map for Plate 5–2. An enlargement of this photograph is in Chapter 5.

Figure 16. Plate 7–5 and map for Plate 7–5. An enlargement of this photograph is in Chapter 7. The line drawing cannot show variations of contrast that are in the photograph. For example, number 21 is the most conspicuous in the photograph, and 86, although important, barely shows in the photograph.

and Tycho we are impressed by the profusion of the plumes mentioned earlier. Copernicus exhibits more of them than Tycho but that may be because the different pre-existing surface affects observations. We observe the plumes as pointed toward the great crater. Usually the point is somewhat brighter than the plume. Sometimes a craterlet can be seen; it can be assumed that a craterlet is always present. The major rays appear to be composed of these plume elements and at some places in them the plumes are easy to disentangle. In the most intense ray to the left from Tycho, the plumes often arise from fairly large craters. Any pre-existing craters, insofar as this hypothesis of ray formation is concerned, may be either endocraters or impact ones. According to the non-ejectus hypothesis, craters formed at the time of the parent explosion are endocraters resulting from the general disturbance brought about by that explosion. Probably these craters lie along faults and in at least many cases are similar to blowhole ones. Such faults will be of two kinds; faults that antedated the great explosion and have merely

been strengthened by its shock waves in the surface rock, and new faults caused by the shattering waves which were strongest in the nimbus and decreased radially. The direction of the plumes would result from a low-density stream of gas issuing like a radial wind from the site of the parent explosion. The cause of the initial explosion is immaterial. The only requirement is that it must have been violent enough to have modified the surrounding surface.

In the cases of the most violent explosions, such as Tycho and Copernicus, the rock was shattered for a considerable distance and faults were opened for hundreds of miles farther. The hypothesis of such an origin demands that lines of craterlets be more common than would be expected through chance. Wherever the direction of the fault approximated to the radial, the plumes necessarily pointed somewhat along the fault line and reinforced each other. The result was a composite great ray in those cases where there were sufficient craters along the fault. The two most intense of the northward rays from Copernicus are among the best examples. In the case of the left hand member of the pair (Plates 7–2, 7–5, and 7–6) we observe the famous line of small craters extending northward from Stadius (89) until it merges with the beginning of that ray. These craters, especially at the northern end of the line, have overlapped sufficiently to form rills, and the rims cast observable shadows when the lighting is right. Within the ray itself we observe a ridge that finally turns right to merge with the second great ray, and continues within it to the ringed plain Lambert (54). Unlike the first great ray, the second one is almost radial. Its southern extension lies in a much rougher area than that of the first ray and is not apparent, but once the background farther north permits the appearance of the ray to become definite, the line of craters all the way to Lambert is conspicuous. The area in Mare Imbrium to the right of the second ray is worth many hours of visual observation and photographic study. Throughout this area the head craterlets of the plumes line up in a beautifully complex pattern. Probably the pattern shows so plainly because it is imposed on the comparatively smooth surface of the dark mare. We can expect manned exploration of the site to show that most of the faults are cracks which resulted from the original cooling of the mare floor and which were opened wider by the shock wave of the Copernican explosion. Lest there be some misunderstanding, it must be stated that there were almost certainly some ejecta from the formations of the greatest craters. The question under discussion is one of dominance. It probably is true that nimbi, such as those of Tycho and Copernicus, owe their present appearance principally to ejecta.

To the left and upper left of Copernicus, beyond the shattered nimbus (Plate 7–5), is a smaller but even more striking area of ray pattern than the one in the mare. Within this area is Stadius (89) which today, whatever it may have been in the past, is little more than a ring of small craters. If previously the formation of the mare had reduced it almost to a "ghost" condition, the Copernican explosion would have tended to produce such craters along the faults of its former rim. Touching Stadius on the south is the mutual point of tangency of two elliptically shaped rays (62 and 63). Their axes extend to the upper left away from Copernicus and the right hand end of the larger is lost in that great

ringed plain. Craters are conspicuous around the perimeters of the ovals; it is possible to count at least 57 small craters around the larger one. These ovals are merely the most conspicuous features of a complex pattern. Many individual plumes can be seen in the area. Straight complex rays, quite commonly originating on one or the other of the ovals, can be seen in about a dozen positions. The pattern certainly is non-accidental and just as certainly it originated with the shock waves of the Copernican explosion. It would appear that pre-existing faults were opened wider and that craterlets formed along them. At first study the oval forms are unexpected. But the area of the larger corresponds well to that of Sinus Aestuum (86) and the shapes also match quite well. The end of Sinus Aestuum toward Copernicus has become ghostlike. It is bounded by Stadius and an arc of the larger oval (62). Quite possibly the two areas are old formations of a similar type. If so, the only difference is that in the case of the oval ray, the formation had become entirely a "ghost" before the birth of Copernicus, which merely opened more widely the faults around the old rim.

The non-ejectus hypothesis accounts nicely for the observed features. We must, however, consider the recent work by Shoemaker. This geologist has made a wide study of terrestrial craters, including Meteorite Crater and manmade explosive ones. He has studied the ejecta from Meteorite Crater and has identified them with respect to positions of origin. In addition to observing these data he has made calculations of the effects of the dynamic forces involved. Following these terrestrial observations he has made measurements of the positions of features connected with the Copernican ray system, and through his calculations has come to the conclusion that they can be accounted for by the ejecta hypothesis. This includes even such features as the lines of small craters and the oval rays. His results appear to be reasonable enough, and if the Copernican data were the only ones available it would be impossible to discriminate between the hypotheses. We would be forced to wait for on-the-site observations.

Plate 10–4 corrects foreshortening at the center of the plate. Its most valuable contribution lies in the interpretation of the features to the right of Tycho for which normally there is much foreshortening and also a large variation in amount. The most important feature shown is the great right hand gap of roughly 130° in the ray "pinwheel." Proclus, in another part of the lunar surface, exhibits a very similar peculiarity. Within this gap is found Mare Humorum. To the south and left of Humorum are found numerous marelike areas, some of them huge. Even the rough parts of the area are less bright than are such regions in general. This region usually is thought of as an extension of Mare Humorum but it would probably be better to consider both it and the mare as extensions of Oceanus Procellarum. There is little question but that these, with Mare Nubium and at least parts of Mare Imbrium, are generically one tremendous ocean. The alignments of craters do give hints of two rays within the region south of Humorum although there is almost no evidence of ray brightening between the craters. One of these cuts the southern shore of Mare Humorum and continues toward the very bright explosion crater, Byrgius, in the same way that one of the rays to the left from Tycho has been described as pointing directly toward Stevinus. Byrgius has a considerable ray system of its own. The cause of the two pinwheel gaps is independent of whether one considers an ejecta hypothesis of ray formation or one due to faulting. In each hypothesis the gap must be due to an extremely high temperature in the area either at the time when the ray system was formed or later. Perhaps Mare Humorum is younger than Tycho. Perhaps it is older but this whole area had not yet had time to cool sufficiently when the great explosion took place. Every serious student of the nature of the lunar surface should make a correlated study of this area, the one to the right of Proclus, the similar one above and to the left of Mare Crisium, Mare Australis, and the region at the left end of Mare Frigoris.

One other Tychonian ray (Plate 5–2) must be discussed, not because of its intrinsic importance but because of the numerous incorrect statements that have been made concerning it. It has been considered as extending to the northern limb and even has been spoken of as the "round the moon" ray. It is not observable in the area near Tycho. The first evidence of it is at "Cassini's Bright Spot" within Deslandres. The ray passes the left hand rim of Albategnius (4) and continues northward to the small ringed plain Hind and the smaller but brighter Hind C

(47). North of Hind the ray is not seen again until the shore of Mare Serenitatis is reached, although the illusion of a ray is preserved by the line of ringed plains Godin (42), Agrippa (3), and Menelaus (59) which is the brightest object along the locus. From Menelaus a ray proceeds northward in Mare Serenitatis to Bessel (11). Although Menelaus does have a small ray system, this ray may belong primarily to Bessel. It is the only conspicuous ray from Bessel and its direction probably has been due to Menelaus. Quite possibly the shock waves from Tycho widened the fault between the craters. The pseudo-ray from Tycho ends in Mare Serenitatis but the pattern is taken up again by four bright craters farther north. Much of this description parallels that of the ray from the left of Tycho to Fracastorius. That one also suffered gaps between craters. However, those were shorter than the long, complete breaks in this case. Of course, it is possible that the existence of Godin, Agrippa, and Menelaus is due to the shock waves from Tycho. In such a case the absence of plumes would be a result of their great distances from Tycho: The outflowing gas stream from Tycho could have had too small a density to affect matters noticeably at that distance.

Plate 11–4, made from one of the Wright globes, shows that the pattern exhibited by the ray triangle of Copernicus, Kepler, and Aristarchus continues to the right. At the time the photograph used for this globe was exposed, librations had carried the bright ringed plain Olbers too close to the limb of the moon for examination, yet its position is shown clearly by the rays that extend to the left from it. Both Neison and Goodacre consider it to have a ray system equal to that of Kepler. The long ray to the right from Kepler is directed toward it and the same is true of the long ray extending in both directions from the southern rim of Seleucus (85).

Any conclusions concerning the nature of the lunar rays probably will remain controversial for several years. The final truth may not be known until after years of thorough, on-the-site exploration. Even today, geologists are much divided concerning some of the terrestrial problems which they have studied at close hand for a good many years. As of now it would appear that although ejecta from the large parent craters did play a minor role in ray formation, small craters in the ray areas were much more important.

15 PECULIAR FEATURES
OF THE SURFACE

One of the basic characteristics of the human mind is the deep urge—really a compulsion—to correlate. The search for correlations and interrelationships is one basis of scientific method and practice: We think of Galileo, Newton, Einstein, and Freud as being very great men because they contributed so much to our known systems of broad correlations. The same unifying tendency is certainly related to the search for a single primary cause of all things, and thereby to theology and metaphysics.

All of this holds true for little problems as well, such as the study of the surface of the moon. The search for correlation causes most current investigators of lunar problems to concentrate on the maria, the mountain-walled plains, and the explosion craters; all of these combine into broad categories with many members each, and thus give rise to fertile generalizations. Very few of the apparently accidental features intrigue most lunar astronomers.

This practice of concentrating on easily correlated features is proper if it is not carried to an extreme. But the peculiar and isolated features deserve consideration too. Someday, on further study, they may well fit into important patterns. "The stone which the builders rejected, the same is become the head of the corner."

Descriptions of some of the more notable unrelated phenomena are set forth below.

1. *Solitary mountains.* One of the rarest of lunar phenomena is the isolated, high mountain rising from comparatively level terrain. There are not many on earth either. Indeed, from their very nature we would expect such mountains to be scarce on either body. Their formation would have required an extremely localized but tremendous force to extrude semi-molten rock (or cinders) that cooled rapidly enough as it was pushed above the surface to keep from collapsing under its own weight. The smaller lunar attraction would make such events somewhat less improbable on the moon than here. There seem to be at least two very fine lunar examples of this unusual phenomenon: Pico and Piton, Plates 3–2 and 10–19, which rise from the lower left floor of Mare Imbrium. Quite a number of low, isolated mountains or hills may also be observed.

The published figures for the heights of mountains and depths of craters on the moon are notoriously inexact. Heights are usually computed by measuring the lengths of shadows. The altitude of the sun above the true horizon can be computed easily for each point of the moon, and the height follows from a simple trigonometric relationship. In application one difficulty is that the sun is not a point and the exact position of the end of the shadow is hard to determine. A second problem arises from the fact that if the shadow terminates in a bright area it appears to be longer than if it ends in a dark zone. Another source of error is the roughness of the ground: if there is high ground nearby the shadows are too short, and if there are depressions they are too long. Theoretically the observer determines only the relative height of the feature being studied above the surface at the end of its shadow. But even this becomes inexact if the shadow ends on a slope either toward or away from the feature.

As a result of these difficulties any hypothesis depending on relative heights, such as the ratio between heights of walls and diameters of craters, must be applied with extreme caution. This trouble is dramatized by the case of Pico (Plate 10–20). Pico is a steep, high mountain standing alone on what appears to be a great plain. It casts a long, sharp shadow the length of which one might think should have been accurately determined long ago. Neison quotes Mädler's determination as a height of 7,060 feet, and Schroeter's, "from three fairly accordant results," as 9,600 feet. The discrepancy is 34% of the smaller estimate! In their recent book Wilkins and Moore give the height as 8,000 feet. Goodacre in 1931 stated merely that it "rises according to various authorities from 7,000 to 9,000 feet above the plain."

Piton, which is just as good an example, is situated in the same area, roughly a hundred miles south and left of Pico; its height is stated as 7,000 feet.

Systematic work on the heights of lunar features has been carried on under the auspices of the United States Air Force. Thousands of photographs have been exposed under time-lapse photography and measured by modern methods. Electronic computers have been used in reducing the data, and computing the heights. The first of

a series of charts has been published. This is a part of man's preparation for a landing on the moon in the near future.

In order to understand the nature of these isolated mountains, one should examine the whole area carefully on the best photographs made soon after sunrise and just before sunset. Three hills and a ridge can be observed south and right of Pico on Plate 10–19. Close examination also shows the ghost of a ringed plain somewhat larger than Plato. Pico lies on this ring. In other words, it is a remainder of a large feature—not a solitary phenomenon. The same story of origin is told, somewhat less clearly, by the environs of Piton. Apparently there was no truly unusual development here.

It is true that the central part of Mare Imbrium was modified by asteroidal impact (Plate 10–22), but all of its section to the left must have resulted from the sinking which is characteristic of all the maria. As described earlier, this sinking produced a great many features: the great Apennine Scarp (Plate 10–18); the "marshy" peninsula extending to the right from it; the marelike floors of Plato and Archimedes, whose rims remained above the sea level; the Caucasian (Plate 3–14) and Alpine (Plate 3–28) scarps; the "Bay of Rainbows" (Plates 10–20 and 10–24) and the ghosts of the area to the left. Pico and Piton are the principal survivors of a former mass of great craters and mountains. If there had been impact here, all these reminders of past glory would have been destroyed.

2. *Valleys.* Despite a wide range in their morphological characteristics, numerous scattered features, varying all the way from very narrow rills to the mountain-walled plain named Schiller, may be grouped under this heading and may be divided into five general categories:

(a) Rills or clefts, for example, Schroeter's Valley.

(b) The Rheita "valley" and the approximation to a valley cutting through the southern part of Snellius.

(c) The Alpine Valley.

(d) The parallel "gashes" or valleys in the Ptolemaeus area.

(e) Schiller.

These divisions are considered in the following paragraphs.

(a) *Rills.* The description given by Neison

nearly a century ago is so excellent that it would be difficult to improve on it, and it is therefore presented verbatim.

"There is one class of formations which have not been placed under any of the three great classes described above, though possessing features rendering them in the highest degree interesting, but which, from unknown nature, cannot well be classified. These are the *rills* or *clefts*, long, narrow, deep ravines, canals or cracks, usually straight, often branched, sometimes curved, and not unusually intersecting one another; extending for considerable distances at times, generally traversing, without interruption, mound, ridge or crater pit in their path, though occasionally deflected by some object, or interrupted by others, when it recommences beyond and proceeds as before. One of the most difficultly visible, they are also one of the most inexplicable formations on the moon, and little information as to their origin can be derived from their situation, which is most diverse, at times lying on the open plains without anything to indicate beginning or end, often running through the midst of mountains, or extending from a crater to the open plain; at others they appear to form an intricate network around a formation, or are situated on the floor of a walled-plain or ring-plain."

Rills vary greatly in breadth and in general their depth is less than their width. In many cases, such as the great rill in Alphonsus, the bottom is illuminated under a high sun. The rill to the lower right of Aristarchus (Plate 7–6) is so broad that it is commonly referred to as "Schroeter's Valley." Others are so narrow that they can be detected only with powerful optical instruments. It is a reasonable speculation that the first men who try to make serious use of the moon will be plagued by thousands of rills too narrow for terrestrial observation.

The distribution of rills over the surface of the moon is by no means uniform, a fact that can hardly be accidental. Rills are not found in the central parts of the maria or in the central parts of the smoothish floors of great mountain-walled plains. Certainly such a finding must be a definite clue to their nature. They are seldom found in the roughest areas either, although they are comparatively common in the somewhat smooth regions separating great mountain masses. The absence of these features in mountainous regions is possibly due, at least in part, to difficulty of observation.

The following paragraphs contain brief descriptions of some typical rills and systems of rills, selected from the approximately 2,000 such objects that have been observed.

Triesnecker-Hyginus-Ariadaeus System (Plate 15–1). This is one of the two greatest rill systems, extending from Triesnecker, near the left hand shoreline of Sinus Medii, to Ariadaeus, on the right hand shore of Mare Tranquillitatis. Much of it lies in a broad, flattish trough south of the Haemus Mountains and north of the great mass separating the Maria Tranquillitatis and Nubium. It is almost at the center of the visible disk.

The shortest but most complex part of the system is related to the ringed plain Triesnecker. Rills are in contact with Triesnecker on three sides, apparently being prevented on the right by Sinus Medii. (Such a distribution is seen in a number of rill systems.) Study of the shadows of the Triesnecker rills shows that they are not all of the same depth. Some craterlets can be observed along them, but not as many as in some other rill systems. Two branches extend northward almost to the nearby rill that runs to the lower right and to the upper left from opposite sides of the conspicuous little crater Hyginus. At proper phases the Hyginus rill is observable even with quite small telescopes. Although craterlets do exist along it, the observer must be on guard against so interpreting the "bridges" or "dams" that cross it to the left of the crater.

The longest of this group of rills is the one that rises near Ariadaeus. It was discovered by Schroeter in 1792 and is very easy to observe. At eight places it appears to tunnel through elevated masses. These may actually be dams formed more recently than the rill, or they may be features that resisted the opening of a fault valley. It will be an interesting task for explorers a few decades from now to determine the exact explanation.

Hesiodus-Ramsden-Hippalus rills (Plates 8–2, 10–1, and 10–5). This triple system is most closely related to Ramsden on the upper right part of the moon. The principal member is a very long, narrow right-left valley that begins at the outer wall of Hesiodus (Plate 8–2) and runs to the right for a couple of hundred miles almost directly toward Ramsden. Near the middle of its course it is interrupted for a long distance by a rather large north-south mountain mass. It reappears to the right of the mass and proceeds as though there had been no interruption. It finally ends at a tiny, bright spot (probably a small hill) left of Ramsden. The complicated rill system in the neighborhood of Ramsden (barely observable on Plate 10–5) reminds one somewhat of the rills near Triesnecker.

From the northern side of Ramsden two conspicuous parallel rills (Plate 10–5) run northward. It is possible that one of them is a continuation of another short rill extending northward into Ramsden. A third rill parallels the first two farther to the right. These three are perhaps the most interesting of their kind on the whole lunar surface. They are lost almost immediately in a mountainous section but reappear regularly wherever there is a depression. All three terminate north of Hippalus, near the left shore of Mare Humorum. The three are broad and equally easy to observe.

Other rills that should be examined by every student are those on the left hand floors of Alphonsus and Arzachel (Plate 16–1). The one in Alphonsus is quite remarkable. It has several intensely black spots with one or more craterlets in each. This rill is considered in detail in the next chapter in connection with residual outgassing from the moon. The rill on the right hand floor of Ptolemaeus is an extension of the ridge that almost cuts the floor of Alphonsus in half. It can be seen best soon after sunrise or long enough before sunset so that the shadow of the right hand wall does not hide it (Plate 11–2). A little to the right of the Straight Wall (Plate 10–2) and almost parallel to it is a rill containing several craterlets. The northern end lies in a black spot and is marked by a craterlet. In the neighborhood of Archimedes (Plate 10–19) there are several rills that are actually rows of contiguous craterlets.

It is a striking fact that, as optical power has increased, the proper use of favorable atmospheric conditions and care and experience in observation bring a marked increase in the proportion of rills seen to exhibit craterlets. Perhaps the first explorers on the spot will find evidences of craterlets in almost all rills. A line of craterlets must usually follow a fault. If two parallel faults are close together, a "graben" type of rill may result between them.

The regions near Tycho and Copernicus show the closest possible relationship between craterlets and rills. The area left of Copernicus viewed at sunrise (Plate 7–1) shows hundreds of craterlets forming patterns that become rills by reason of mere contiguity. Plate 7–2 shows the same characteristic somewhat less noticeably on the right side of Copernicus. Rills also exist radially on the slope of this feature. Many lines of radial, contiguous craterlets are conspicuous on the rather flat floors of walled plains to the lower left of Tycho. Plate 8–7, which exhibits these, is worthy of much study.

A general rule is that a craterlet may be found wherever a rill makes a sharp turn or crosses another rill. There are a very few apparent exceptions to the rule, but even in these

Plate 15–1. The Triesnecker-Hyginus-Ariadaeus rill system. See Plate 3–1 for technical details.

Plate 15–2. Features of upper left moon outlined for use as a map. See Plate 4–3 for technical details.

Plate 15–3. Details of upper left moon (see Plate 15–2). See Plate 4–3 for technical details.

cases tiny craterlets may possibly exist. Moreover, there may well have been complete destruction of a craterlet during the evolution of broad rills.

There is also a rather noticeable relationship between rills and major rays. Both in general seem to follow faults, which usually exhibit what may be "blow-hole" craterlets or even, good-sized craters, Plate 8–4, as in the case of Tycho's great left land ray.

(b) *The Rheita Valley and its surroundings.* One of the two best known valleys of the moon, it is located in the upper left hand quadrant, which contains some of the finest examples of sunken areas to be found outside the maria. Plate 15–2 shows part of the region marked to identify the most interesting features. Plate 15–3 is from the same photograph. Some of the numerous unnamed sunken areas are designated by the letter S.

Plates 15–4 and 15–5, made respectively near sunrise and sunset, demonstrate that the "valley" is merely a deep trench along the left hand part of a depression so wide that it could be con-

sidered a shallow mountain-walled plain. Plate 15–4, made at phase 4.1 days with grazing sunlight, reveals that the valley itself is composed of several confluent craters of varying sizes whose mutual walls have mostly collapsed. Except for these craters, no sign of any sort of explosion, either of internal or impact origin, is observable. Directly north of Rheita on this plate the barely rising sun reveals a very large and rather square depression with walls so low that it disappears in less than a day; it is more difficult to observe than even Deslandres.

Another of the many interesting features of these plates is a long, low scarp revealed as extending northward from Janssen. Its true nature is demonstrated by Plates 15–3 and 15–5, which show it dark at sunrise but bright at sunset. This shows that the ground has sunk to the right. Scarps, sometimes several hundred miles long, can be seen throughout the southern section of the moon at advantageous phases.

Plates 15–2 and 15–3 show a long, narrow right-left, slightly sunken area crossing the southern part of Snellius.

(c) *The Alpine Valley.* The origin of this great valley, connecting the Maria Frigoris and Imbrium, has been the subject of wide differences of opinion. It runs in a direction slightly up to the right toward Imbrium for about 75 miles, with a width of about four to six miles.

The top photograph of Plate 15–6 shows the valley under a morning sun, the second under an afternoon sun. The third (an early morning view) was made by infrared light at the 60-inch reflector. This feature begins as a narrow valley touching a dome and a crater. It then turns and, after somewhat less than a quarter of its length, suddenly widens. The morning photographs especially show the line of small craters along the southern rim to best advantage. The marelike floor is shown fairly well by the last picture. Unlike the Rheita Valley and many of the rills, this valley appears definitely to be a graben. The photographs seem to contradict two of the suggestions that have been made in explanation of its origin: that it is the result of a confluent line of craters and that it is a valley plowed out by some huge meteorite.

(d) *The parallel valleys in the Ptolemaeus area.* There are numerous narrow valleys in this area (Plate 11–1) that have been interpreted by some able students as gashes cut by fragments of an asteroid assumed to have struck first in the Mare Imbrium area. The principal one of these markings is shown as Plate 15–7. It is roughly 150 miles long and ends in the right wall of Alphonsus.

It is suggested that a very careful study be made of this plate which shows the structural details of the principal member of the system. It hardly seems possible that this can have been plowed out by any sort of missile.

The best guess today is that the "gashes" were opened along faults at the time of the sinkings that produced both the Maria Imbrium and Tranquillitatis.

late 15–4. Note unnamed, large, squarish depression on terminator north of Rheita. Has general characteristics of very shallow mountain-walled plain. See Plate 4–2 for technical details.

Plate 15–5. Late afternoon, for comparison with morning lighting of Plate 15–3. See Plate 6–2 for technical details.

Plate 15–6. (Top) Alpine Valley in morning. See Plate 4–10 for technical details. (Middle) Alpine Valley in afternoon. See Plate 6–4 for technical details. (Bottom) Mt. Wilson and Palomar Observatories, 1957 August 4^d 04^h 20^m UT, phase 7.88 days, colongitude 10°. Alpine Valley in very early morning.

Any satisfactory hypothesis accounting for these peculiar valley-like features must not neglect the following data:

i. The "gashes" are approximately parallel to each other.

ii. They are parallel to the right and left walls of Ptolemaeus and to the great rill at the right edge of its floor.

iii. They are parallel to the great ridge on the floor of Alphonsus, to a conspicuous rill on this same floor, and to the greater part of a still more prominent rill at the extreme left, Plate 11–2.

iv. The valley-like features are parallel to rills of craterlets on the northern floor of Ptolemaeus.

v. They are rather closely parallel to the Straight Wall, which forms part of the left hand shore of Mare Nubium, Plate 11–1.

vi. They are approximately perpendicular to the slope gradient between Mare Nubium and Mare Tranquillitatis.

(e) *Schiller*. This walled plain (Plate 8–9) is so much elongated that it borders on the valley type of feature. Because of its nearness to the limb, foreshortening distorts it very much. The picture exhibits its rim craterlets strongly and quite definitely indicates that it is a graben-like formation.

Plate 15–7. The greatest of the so-called "gashes" in the general
Ptolemaeus area. See Plate 12–3 for technical details.

3. *Messier and W. H. Pickering.* This controversial pair of twin craters illustrates excellently how varying shadows distort features and cause misunderstandings. It has actually been argued that these craters change size and shape during the month. Plate 15–8, from Lick Observatory photographs made at different phases, tells the story rather completely:

(a) A saucer-like depression exists, partly between the two craters.

(b) The southern ray is a series of bright spots; the northern one, under some illuminations, is observed to branch near the middle of its course, with a very faint component turning slightly northward.

(c) The two main rays are tangent not only to W. H. Pickering but also to another crater of approximately the same size farther right. This crater on the right, especially under a morning sun, is less conspicuous than are the others, but only because of the light background. In the afternoon it is more nearly comparable.

(d) The second of the four pictures shows three more craters of about the same size farther right on the same line. These may be merely coincidental.

(e) Bright spots similar to the line of the southern ray usually indicate craterlets.

By way of conclusion: A right-left fault line probably exists in the surface rock and a minimum of three endocraters have formed along it, with "blowhole" craterlets along the southern ray. If this is true, there is nothing mysterious about the pair of objects.

Plate 15–8. Messier and W. H. Pickering with their ray system throughout the month. See Plates 4–2, 4–3, 6–1, and 6–2 for technical details.

16 RESIDUAL OUTGASSING

The resurgence of serious interest in the moon that followed World War II focused attention on the problem of "outgassing," the release of gas from the lunar interior. One of the strangest cases involves the crater Linné.

Linné was discovered by Riccioli during the seventeenth century; Lohrman, Mädler, and Schmidt all observed it as a crater. Schmidt drew it as a crater in eight of eleven drawings he made between 1840 and 1843. In 1866, however, he made the spectacular announcement that the crater no longer remained and that only the bright mound was observable. During 1867 numerous observers could find only the mound. Late in that year Schmidt announced that he could discern a mountain in the center of the mound. During 1868 Knott, Buckingham, and Key observed a shallow depression at the center. Later a craterlet was detected by Secchi, who estimated its diameter at barely half a mile. Still later Huggins measured its diameter as two miles. Since that time Linné has been observed, when near the terminator, more or less easily through large telescopes.

In a rather recent program hundreds of pairs of photographs have been made of the lunar sur-face. The two plates of each pair were exposed with a minimum time interval between them. One of the two plates used only violet and blue light, and the other used infrared light almost exclusively.

The Linné mound has been photographed on some of these dual plates. An infrared exposure is reproduced as Plate 10–15, and its blue-violet mate as Plate 10–16. Both show the surface of the right part of Mare Serenitatis nicely, but the infrared plate is distinctly the better. Because the moon has no appreciable atmosphere, this difference in over-all clarity must be due to the terrestrial atmosphere; the passage of the light through the lower air of the earth absorbs and scatters the shorter violet waves more than it does the longer red ones.

The craterlet on the Linné mound shows sharply in the infrared (Plate 10–15), but is invisible in the blue-violet (Plate 10–16). The difference in Linné's appearance is greater than one would expect from examination of the rest of the plate, although it is not enough to make it absolutely certain that it is not merely an accidental effect from our own atmosphere. If the effect is in fact not due to the terrestrial atmosphere, it must be from something on the moon itself. The reasonable assumption in such a case is the existence of a slight haze between the craterlet and the observer. Such a haze might be either dust or gas, or both. The hypothesis of a dust cloud can no longer be considered favorably, but a very low density of gas leaking from the craterlet would be almost completely ionized by sunlight. The ionization makes it lu-

minous and also increases its scattering effect on light passing through it, especially on the shorter wavelengths.

Indeed, a gas only one-billionth as dense as earth's sea-level atmosphere could produce a noticeable effect. It appears rather probable, but not certain, that there is such a residual outgassing from Linné. The fact that such able nineteenth-century astronomers as Schmidt, Secchi,

Plate 16–1. Mt. Wilson and Palomar Observatories, (left) 1956 October 26^d 12^h 54^m UT, Kodak II–O plate, no filter; (right) two minutes later with Kodak I–N plate and infrared filter; phase 22.35 days, colongitude 177°. Possible obscuration of lower left floor of Alphonsus.

and Huggins believed that they had observed changes makes the evidence for such a conclusion much more convincing than if the current observations pertained merely to some previously unobserved craterlet. If the crater disappeared as described, there was much more of such outgassing for several months in 1866 than has occurred since.

Any photographic investigation of lunar outgassing can be carried out only on nights when our atmosphere is unusually steady. Otherwise any small effect from the moon would be added to a very large effect from the instability of the earth's air, and could not be properly evaluated. If we could carry out observations from above the terrestrial atmosphere the lunar effect would be the only one observable, and each pair of plates would tell the whole story.

Predawn seeing conditions at Mount Wilson on the morning of October 26, 1956, were unusually good. Four pairs of plates were made that night of the area from Ptolemaeus through Tycho. An obscuration of the lower left part of the floor of Alphonsus was evident on the blue-violet plates. Its reality was checked on all four pairs by using Arzachel and other parts of Alphonsus as controls. Plate 16–1 is one of the four pairs taken on this date. Each observer must decide for himself whether there is a significantly greater loss in the blue light along the northern part of the rill on the floor to the left than there is in other places. Such a loss, of course, would suggest outgassing from this rill, which contains the famous black spots of Alphonsus with one or more craterlets at the center of each.

Publication of this Alphonsus result led the Soviet astronomer Dr. N. A. Kozyrev of the Pulkovo Observatory to one of the most provocative observations in modern lunar astronomy. He made a spectrographic study of the region, using the 50-inch reflector of the Crimea Observatory with a prism spectrograph. On the night of November 3, 1958, with lunar phase conditions almost the same as they had been when the haze was observed in 1956, the slit of his spectrograph was extended right and left across the central peak of Alphonsus, as shown in Plate 16–2. The lines of the spectrum are images of the slit of the spectrograph and of a very narrow strip of the image of any object which has been projected on it. Plate 16–2 shows the position of the slit

as used by Kozyrev for these observations. Each line of the spectrum actually is a picture of the narrow strip of the moon which here is hidden by the ink of the line used to represent it. Each line, therefore, must get brighter where the moon is brighter along this strip. Near the bottom of the slit is the bright, broad image of the wall of Alphonsus. Therefore the spectrogram must show a broad, bright band running across all of the lines of the spectrogram. Our photograph of the spectrogram is a negative, therefore we see this band as a dark one. The craterlet which Kozyrev was observing is projected near the middle of the slit. To the extent that any spectrogram differs from that of the sun it must have been affected by some lunar characteristic. If a significant change should be temporary it would indicate a temporary action of some sort on the moon. What Kozyrev reported was a spectrogram that showed luminescence which must belong to the moon instead of the sun. A copy of the translation of his letter to the author is translated for the reader in the appendix.

Unfortunately the accounts of Dr. Kozyrev's observations, as reported in our newspapers, suffered both from omission of pertinent data and from language difficulties. It would have been far better if the exciting word "eruption" had not been used. Technically it is correct, but the image which it brings to mind is not. The "eruption" was not an explosion but a half-hour-long discharge of very low-pressure gas from a craterlet atop the central mountain of Alphonsus.

The numbers which have been placed over Kozyrev's spectra are the wavelengths as used by physicists. If one looks at the top spectrum (Kozyrev's Number 2) he notices that the negative is darker near the middle of the lines than it is for the same positions in the other two spectra. This is the position where, for all three spectra, the light falls from the central craterlet of Alphonsus. The darkening of the negative is especially noticeable for the general section between about 4,000 and 4,800. There is no question but that additional light was coming from the region of the craterlet when this picture was made, more than when the ones just before and after were exposed. The only reasonable explanation is that a low density gas, ionized by the sunlight, was escaping for about half an hour from this craterlet.

Plate 16–2. Position of slit and negative of Kozyrev spectrograms of gas discharge in Alphonsus.

Although there is no question about the emission shown in the continuum, nevertheless identification of the Swan bands is less certain. These are emission bands from molecules composed of two atoms of carbon, and are commonly found in cometary spectra where the molecules have been excited by solar radiation. Such gases in a comet must be of almost unbelievably low density. Kozyrev has estimated from his spectrogram that the density of the gas at the opening of the craterlet was in the neighborhood of a billionth of that of our air at sea level. This low density is sufficient to produce the observed effect and also that of the direct photographs of October 26, 1956.

Although it would be important to confirm the Swan spectrum in Dr. Kozyrev's observation, the fact that an emission spectrum existed, no matter what the source, is much more so. With the possible exception of the Russian photographs of the far side of the moon, Kozyrev's spectrum is the most important single lunar observation ever made.

When all data from every source are considered, it seems to be almost certain that at least some residual outgassing still takes place on the moon. Perhaps there is quite a lot of activity of this kind, but at present it seems best to accept only instances that cannot be denied, and to leave more far-ranging speculations to the future, when more data will be available.

The problem of outgassing and the current uncertainty regarding its frequency demonstrate the need for a really systematic program of lunar observation. Our lunar programs are seriously handicapped by lack of sufficient systematic data.

The startling data which have been received through use of our space vehicles tend to produce a belief that rather few terrestrially based observations will be needed in the future. It is easy to look at the pictures which have been transmitted from space and to forget that they represent only a minor part of the surface, even of that of nearside. Study by astronomers who are actually on the lunar surface will be much circumscribed at first. Observations made simultaneously over the whole of nearside can be secured only from the earth. The old-time program of direct photography through use of large telescopes should be expanded, not curtailed. However, it must be modified by adoption of all available new and useful technological aids. For example, instead of the use of two broad spectrographic regions, as was done in the initial program, mentioned earlier in this chapter, future pictures must be secured through the use of narrow-band pass filters at several spectral frequencies. Those plates that most completely furnish the needed data must be studied in conjunction with the pictures returned from space. Each group has a contribution to make.

There is no truly satisfactory scale of brightness for lunar features. The present obsolescent scale, described in Chapter 2, should be replaced. Accurate knowledge of relative brightnesses is essential to any program involving study of possible lunar changes. A photometric program also has much value in studies of the origin of the surface features. Approximately a hundred of the most important areas should be measured by use of modern photometric equipment, at small intervals of colongitude, throughout the month and the variations of albedo should be catalogued for each. Corrections for librations should be included in the case of all features near the limb.

All intensely black and intensely bright craterlets should be investigated spectrographically throughout each month, as should such ringed plains as Alphonsus, Aristarchus, and Plato. Only through such a comprehensive program does there appear to be much chance of gaining knowledge concerning sites of outgassing and of the frequencies of its occurrence. Such a program should also locate the principal conditions of luminescence that may exist in craters, rays, scarps, and other topographic phenomena.

All results should be carefully correlated with observations that have been made by instruments used either on or near the moon. Every type of physical datum that can be obtained must be secured from both the moon itself and the space near it.

17 TIDES TODAY AND

THROUGH THE AGES

The friction of the tides pulling against the surface of the earth slows the earth's rotation, and this in turn gradually affects the apparent motion of the moon around the earth. The tidal forces also produce, although with almost infinite slowness, tremendous changes in the moon's actual orbit. Indeed, all the ordinary perturbations to which that orbit is subject, except the one due to the equatorial bulge of the earth, are attributable to forces which we might consider tidal.

An elementary explanation of tides is easy enough, but a thorough study of them is the work of a lifetime. A rather simple tidal theory was worked out by the great French astronomer and mathematician, Laplace. George Darwin, the astronomer son of Charles Darwin, contributed four large volumes of research and summarized them in one much smaller and less technical book. Of course long before Laplace the great Newton saw that the tides were implicit in his laws, and gave a first simple explanation of them that tells enough for some purposes.

Contrary to what one might expect, tides tend to be high when the moon is at its highest, and also when it is 180 degrees away, high over the opposite side of the earth. The tide is low when the moon is near the horizon. If the oceans were deep enough and had smooth floors with no islands or continents, and if the earth rotated slowly, we would experience the highest tide almost exactly when the moon is nearest the zenith and when it is 180 degrees from the zenith, and low tide with the moon on the horizon. The lack of these ideal conditions is responsible for the lags that produce most of the complications.

What seems surprising is that there should be a high tide when the moon is farthest from, as well as at, the zenith. This is because we tend to think of the earth as a hard ball with a rubber skin of oceans around it, and we think of the moon as reaching out hands to grasp and to pull on it. The rubber skin, by this analogy, would be pulled out somewhat to produce a high tide on the side toward the moon and would be stretched tight, or thin, on the opposite side, producing a low tide there.

But all of this thinking is incorrect. As Newton stated, "every particle attracts every other particle . . .", so each particle of the moon is pulling each particle of the earth. It does not matter a bit whether the particles are in our air, our oceans, or our rivers, on the "solid" surface or deep inside the core of the earth. Each one of them is pulled by each particle anywhere within the moon. In turn each terrestrial particle pulls each lunar particle just as strongly.

If this were all there were to the law there would be no tides, no matter how strongly the moon pulled on the earth. The tides result from the relation Newton expressed in the words that follow immediately upon his phrase quoted above: ". . . inversely as the square of the distance."

In Figure 17, A and B are two equal particles, one in the ocean, the other near it in the "solid" core of the earth. C is any particle of the same mass near the center of the earth, about 4,000 miles farther from the moon than are A and B. D and E are near each other and about 4,000 miles still farther from the moon than the earth's center. The moon pulls A and B by the same amount, and so they tend to "fall" the same distance toward the moon each second. The moon pulls on C less strongly because C is 4,000 miles farther away, so C does not tend to fall as far as the first particles. Consequently, the distance AC increases, and we have a high tide at A. Since D and E are 4,000 miles farther than C from the moon, they tend to fall less than does C and as a result we have a high tide at E also; the center of the earth is pulled away from the water at E. The low tides, then, must be on a great circle around the earth and half way between A and E.

If the whole of the earth were fluid, like the oceans, it would be very difficult to detect the tides. We would have no ocean bottom to help us. Of course this is not the case; most of the earth is part of what can be considered, in this context, a rigid sphere. B, C, and D are tied together by the earth's rigidity and must fall toward the moon by nearly the same amount, even though they are pulled differently by the satellite. The average of the effects on B and D equals the amount C tends to fall. But because A and E are both fairly free from other particles in the ocean, they fall toward the moon by approximately the amounts demanded by their distances. As a result the ocean must get deeper at

A and at E. A moves a bit away from B because B is tied to C, and D moves away from E because D is tied to C. Actually the solid part of the earth is not perfectly rigid, and the distances CB and CD do change by about six inches twice a day. Our houses rise and fall in this manner all the time.

This explanation applies to points A and E, where the moon is passing through the zenith. These points are always in or near the tropics of the earth. In areas near the poles where the moon cannot pass through the zenith, tidal forces are never as great as they can be in the tropics. At the poles the moon must always be low in the sky and when it is at the celestial equator, twice a month, there must theoretically be a continuous low tide at the poles all day long.

The tidal force, then, is merely the difference between two forces. One of these is the moon's attraction on a particle at the center of the earth, the other its attraction on a particle at the point on the surface where we are studying the tide. It can be shown from Newton's law, using only college freshman algebra, that the tidal force varies approximately as the inverse cube of the moon's distance from the earth. If the moon were twice as close, the force would be eight times as great. If it were twice as far away, it would be one eighth what it is. During each month the moon's distance varies between 221,000 and 253,000 miles, and of course this is enough to cause the very noticeable monthly variation in tidal force.

The sun pulls the earth about 160 times as strongly as does the moon, but it is 400 times as far away and so its tidal force is only about two fifths as great. In other words the difference between the sun's pull on A and on C is only two fifths of the difference between the moon's pull

Figure 17. Tides caused by the moon.

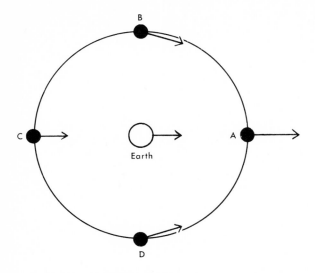

Figure 18. Effect of the sun on moon's orbit.

on those points when both the sun and moon are at the zenith. The inverse cube law cuts down the tidal force very rapidly.

All of this is very much complicated in practice by a variety of other effects: the combinations of lunar and solar tides, the shallowness of oceans, blocking or obstructing of tides by islands and continents, and the shapes of shorelines and other terrestrial factors.

The sun's perturbing force on the moon's orbit, which is actually another tidal force, with the earth and the moon as the particles affected, is illustrated in Figure 18, in which the moon is of course much too close to the earth. When the moon is at A, the sun pulls more strongly on each particle of the moon than it does on similar particles of the earth. Therefore, it pulls the moon away from the earth. When the moon is at C the sun pulls the earth away from the moon. When the moon is at either B or D the pull of the sun on each particle of it is about as strong as the pull on the earth's particles, but the directions of the attractions toward the sun's center converge in the direction of the sun's pull on the earth. As a result, the sun tends to pull the earth and moon a little closer together at such times. This effect, evident near the half moon phase, is like the low-tide effect referred to in earlier parts of this same chapter.

The perturbations of the moon's orbit by the sun are complicated by several other factors. The

moon's distance from the earth varies during the month, the sun is in the plane of the moon's orbit at only two instants during the month, and the sun's distance from the earth changes during the year. These three complications cause many periodic terms affecting the orbit of the moon. In addition to the sun each one of the planets is pulling on the earth and moon and creates a very slight perturbation. E. W. Brown in his great study of the moon's orbit included more than 650 such terms in his lunar tables.

The two most important of these many perturbations affect our calculation of eclipses very much. In Figure 19, showing the elements of the moon's orbit, the line FB, along which the plane of the earth's orbit around the sun and the plane of the moon's orbit around the earth intersect each other, is called the *line of nodes*. The line AP, which joins the two points P and A where the moon is respectively closest and farthest from the earth during each month, is called the *line of apsides*. If there were no perturbations, these lines would always point in the same direction in space. But the perturbations do exist, and because of them these lines revolve. The line of apsides turns forward at an irregular rate in the plane of the moon's orbit, requiring on the average a trifle less than nine years (8.8503) to go around once and return to its original position. The line of nodes turns backward in the ecliptic (the plane of the earth's orbit), reaching its original position in 18.5995 years. An eclipse takes place only when the moon is close enough to one of its nodes at the instant of full or of new moon. Moreover, a total solar eclipse can occur only when the moon is not too far from perigee, the point in its orbit where it is closest to the earth. When it is far from perigee its angular diameter is less than that of the sun, and hence it cannot completely obscure the sun. The effects of these perturbations on the prediction of eclipses are described simply in Chapters 20 and 21 of *Pictorial Astronomy* (Thomas Y. Crowell Co.).

The tides cause constant friction between the ocean waters and the solid portion of the earth. Because the month is longer than the day, this friction slows down the earth's rotation. If the month were shorter than the day the friction would speed up the rotation. If the day and month were equal the areas of highest tide would not change on the earth and there would be no friction. Two thousand years ago a day was about $\frac{1}{50}$ second shorter than it is now. So the average day of the last 2,000 years was $\frac{1}{100}$ second shorter than a day is now. Multiplying $\frac{1}{100} \times 365 \times 2000$ we find that 2,000 years ago the position of any point on earth, in terms of the globe's rotation, was displaced by 7,300 seconds of time, or about two hours, from where it would have been if the length of day had been constant. The displacement 4,000 years ago was about eight hours. This displacement affects the times of occurrence of eclipses of the sun and their positions on the surface of the earth to such an extent that even some of the imperfect ancient eclipse records can be used to check the change in rotation.

The effect of the tides in slowing down the earth's rotation decreases the energy of the rotation and involves us with another universal law of physics, one that is as important as the law of gravitation. This is the law of conservation of energy: Energy can neither be created nor destroyed.

Energy can, of course, appear in many forms and can be changed from one form to another. The most condensed form by far is as matter.

(We even know the exact relationship between grams of matter and ergs of energy.) Energy can also appear as motion (kinetic energy), as energy of position (potential energy), as work done, as electricity or heat, or in still other forms. The amount of work done on a body measures the change in its energy. Since energy cannot be created or destroyed, if energy is taken from one place, as it is when the tides slow the rotation of the earth, it must automatically appear in some other place. A little of the lost energy of rotation becomes heat energy and is radiated into space. The remainder must stay somewhere in the earth-moon system. When it is tracked down mathematically it is discovered to be at work pushing the earth and moon farther and farther apart! This change in the moon's distance is very slow. But if humanity can maintain its existence and its interest long enough to observe the development, the moon will one day be seen twice as far away as it is now and the tidal force will be only an eighth as strong. Once, far away in the past, the moon must have been at half its present distance, exerting tidal forces eight times what they are now upon an earth spinning far more rapidly than it does today. But this is part of the story of the evolution of the moon.

Figure 19. The orbit of the moon in respect to the ecliptic.

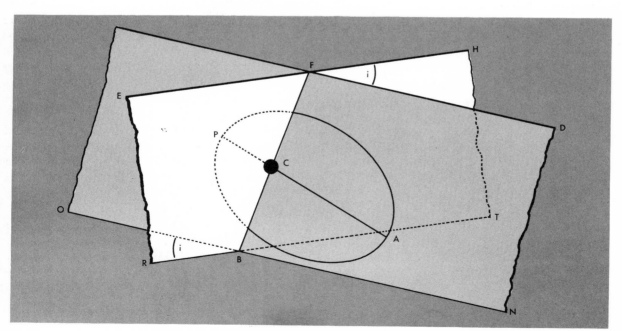

18 THE EVOLUTION OF THE MOON

Our moon is a freak among the satellites of the solar system. It is true that Jupiter and Saturn do have some moons which are larger than our moon but those planets are huge. When we consider ratios of masses of satellites to their primaries none of them is even comparable to that of our moon. If there were astronomers on other planets we can be certain that their name for us would be "The Double Planet." It is a freak in a second manner. The two satellites of Mars move almost exactly in the plane of that planet's equator. One of them diverges by half a degree, the other by only a thirtieth of that tiny amount. Four of the five inner satellites of Jupiter are so nearly in the plane of that body's equator that the difference is not measurable. The fifth diverges by less than half a degree. The seven satellites which are closest to Saturn also have orbits which lie practically in the plane of Saturn's equator. The third satellite has the greatest inclination and that is merely a trifling 66 minutes of arc. The case of Uranus is even more spectacular. The orbit plane and the planet's equator are almost perpendicular to each other. The five satellites move in the equatorial plane, insofar as we are able to determine. Our moon's orbit around the earth lies rather close to the earth's orbit around the sun. The angle between the plane of the moon's orbit and the plane of the earth's equator varies between 18½ and 28½ degrees in a period of about 18.6 years.

In shape of its orbit the moon also exhibits the same sort of freakishness. Its orbit is quite eccentric, the distance from the earth varying between 221,000 and 253,000 miles during the month. Neither of the satellites of Mars has even half this eccentric an orbit. All five of the inner satellites of Jupiter have orbits which are practically circular. The outer seven, which probably are captured asteroids, all have orbits with greater eccentricities. The six inner satellites of Saturn all have orbits which are less eccentric than that of our moon and only the sixth has even half the eccentricity. The satellites of Uranus all have orbits which differ only negligibly from circularity.

Much about the evolution of the moon can be deduced from the physical laws governing tides, which were discussed in the previous chapter. In that chapter we considered briefly the law of conservation of energy. This is the law which makes it impossible in the physical universe to get something for nothing. It is the law which prevents our everyday lives from undergoing the freakishness of nightmares. Closely related to energy is *momentum,* a useful quantity which possibly we could consider as having been invented by man. It is defined as the product of the mass (amount of material in a body) multiplied by its velocity.

Directly related to momentum is *moment of momentum.* For a revolving object, this is the momentum of the object multiplied by the radius of its orbit. Momentum itself is not conserved the way energy is, but moment of momentum is conserved.

A familiar example from everyday life illustrates the conservation of moment of momentum. Figure skaters often twirl on the point of one skate. The skater usually starts slowly, with arms outstretched. This is even more spectacular if he holds a weight in each hand. Then he brings his arms close to his body—and spins faster. The increased speed results from conservation of moment of momentum: he has reduced his radius of rotation and to keep the moment constant, his velocity must increase. If he raises his arms, he will spin more slowly again.

The same situation applies to the earth and moon. They form a rotating, two-body system. The sum of their moments of momentum must remain constant except for the fact that small amounts of energy are lost to space. Thus the loss in moment of momentum of the earth, due to tidal friction, must be equaled by the gain in the moon's moment of momentum. The equations are too complicated to justify inclusion here. Momentum is defined as the product of mass times velocity. The equations describing energy and momentum will not be used in this discussion, but they do make the relationships clear: when E represents energy of motion (kinetic energy), M stands for momentum, m is the mass and v the velocity of a body, then $M = mv$ and $E = \frac{1}{2}mv^2 = \frac{1}{2}Mv$.

The lunar orbital moment of momentum is at present almost five times that of the earth's rotation, but the sum of the moon's and the earth's moments must remain essentially constant. From these relationships we can tell how much the month will lengthen for any given change in the length of the day. It has been determined that although both the day and the month are increasing, the day is lengthening

more rapidly. This produces a tendency for the day and the month eventually to become equal. It follows that if the changes continue long enough the earth will eventually keep one face toward the moon at all times. The tides have already produced this condition on our much smaller companion. Such an equality would come when the day and month have both become about 47 of our present days long.

The word "tendency" was used deliberately in the preceding paragraph. If the oceans were to freeze, the tidal friction would decrease to a rather small fraction of what it is now. This would very much lessen the rate of change and increase the time necessary to produce the final effect. Under our present view of stellar evolution it appears very unlikely that such freezing will ever take place. Still, the whole process is so slow that the earth and moon may not last long enough to attain this equality of day and month.

As the day approaches the month in length, the effect of the lunar tides in lengthening both periods must decrease. If they were to become equal the tidal effect would vanish, for there would then be fixed tides on both bodies and

Figure 20. Relative sizes of satellites. The largest satellites of earth, Jupiter, Saturn, Uranus, and Neptune are shown. The large circle represents successively each of these planets as compared to its largest satellite.

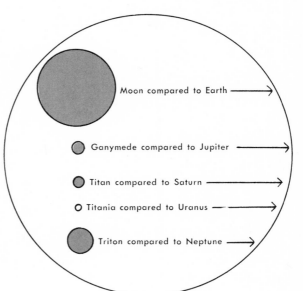

155

therefore no friction. If the earth and moon could then be left alone the system would be stable—at least we do not know today of anything that would change it from within itself. But all of the foregoing conclusions have ignored the fact that the sun is in the picture too. Its tidal forces on the earth and moon will also have decreased, but at a far lesser rate. The friction of those solar tidal forces on the earth cannot become zero unless the day and the year become equal. With a decrease in the lunar tidal effect the solar tides will eventually become by far the more important tidal factor. They slow down the day without having a long-term effect on the distance between the earth and the moon. This speeds up the time when the day and the month become equal, and if at that point in time the solar tides were to cease, nothing more would happen.

However, the solar tides have a far longer course to run than do their lunar counterparts. They continue to lengthen the day with almost no effect on the month, so the day must eventually become the longer of the two periods. When this happens, the lunar tidal effect must immediately come into existence again. However, now the friction must drag ahead instead of backwards. The conservation of moment of momentum will draw the moon in and thus shorten the month. Nevertheless, the day will remain always the longer. Eventually (if the earth and moon last long enough) the day and the month will both be much shorter than they are now. The moon will be much closer than it is and the tides will be tremendous. When the moon's distance has diminished to one fifth today's value the tidal force will be 125 times as great as it is today.

All this has led some writers (not scientists) to predict that the moon will crash into the earth. Indeed some enthusiasts apparently expect this to happen while man still lives here! They forget, or else never knew, that inverse cube factor of tidal forces. At some future time while the surfaces of the earth and moon are on the average still about a thousand miles apart, the earth's tidal force on the moon will become greater than the gravitational force that holds the moon together. Astronomers call the distance at which this occurs "Roche's limit." At this distance disruption of the moon must begin. Unless the moon's own substance produces very violent explosions, the tidal force will disrupt the lunar surface, continually working its disruption deeper and deeper. We do not know whether the catastrophe will come as a sudden explosion or as a great cracking of the lunar surface that for a time leaves the primary mass little affected. Gradually, however, all the material which now composes the moon will separate to form a ring around the earth somewhat similar to one of the rings of Saturn.

The earth's greater gravitational force would prevent its being shattered at the time of the moon's destruction, although the immense tides would probably change its whole surface permanently. During the time of destruction the scattering of the lunar fragments would very rapidly lessen the tidal force. Then the system would become quite stable, except insofar as the solar tides increase the distance from the sun, with a consequent gradual lengthening of both the day and the year. It must be remembered constantly, however, that because of the tremendous time factor involved we do not expect these later events ever actually to take place.

Some people have suggested that the rings of Saturn were formed in this manner by a number of satellites approaching too close to a primary. But it seems to be certain that the particles composing these rings were always close to Saturn and that they never were united as one or more normal moons. One of the moons of Mars is even now on its way in to the planet. It is so small, though, that tidal forces are unlikely ever to shatter it.

George Darwin used this tidal process as a basis of his suggestion that the moon evolved from the primitive gaseous earth. His hypothesis was regarded with much favor for a good many years, but today, despite its apparent plausibility, it probably has little except historical importance.

Darwin carried his tidal calculations backward through unknown ages to arrive at an era when the day and month were equal and the earth and moon were very close together. (He made the implicit assumption that the earth-moon system had existed for a long enough time.) He could not state the length of that original day-month more accurately than between three and five of our present hours. With earth and moon very close together, he believed, the tremendous tides must have formed a bridge connecting the two bodies. With day and month equal there would be no tidal friction and, unless there were interference from outside forces, the configuration would have continued indefinitely. However, the resulting equilibrium would have been very unstable, quickly upset by the solar tides. As soon as any inequality developed there would be tremendous tidal friction that would begin the moving-apart process which he had followed in reverse.

To account for the nature of the earth and moon prior to the era reached by his calculation backward in time, Darwin had two possible starting points. He found that if the earth had been a highly compressible gas, with at most a rather small, dense core, one evolution process had been followed. If the earth had been a fairly incompressible fluid or even a gas that was not highly compressible, the development had been along different lines.

The first of these processes may, in fact, have formed the inner moons of Jupiter, Saturn, and Uranus, and conceivably of Mars. If a planet is composed of a perfect gas or if it has a deep enough gaseous atmosphere around a comparatively small core, and if it rotates fast enough, it will require all the force of its gravitation merely to retain its equatorial particles. If such a planet is shrinking it must, like the spinning skater who slowly lowers his arms, be rotating at a continually increasing speed. This is demanded by the law of conservation of angular momentum. With this increase in speed the weight of particles on its equator decreases. If it rotates fast enough gravitation becomes inadequate, and it can no longer hold completely the outer equatorial molecules. In other words the weight of the outer equatorial particles has become zero. Therefore it leaves them behind as it shrinks still more. Eventually the planet must become very oblate, that is, much flattened at the poles, with a disklike equator. As shrinkage continues, more and more equatorial matter must be left behind. This is shown qualitatively in the upper line of Figure 21; each successive figure in it shows the result of a more rapid rotation than does the one to its left. Gradually these discarded particles may collect to form a satellite, which must move very nearly in the plane of the planet's equator. We would expect a moon formed in this manner to be of negligible size with respect to its primary and to move in a nearly circular orbit. Quite a number of planetary satellites do show these characteristics.

Figure 21. Shapes of rotating fluids. Figures of equilibrium of gaseous bodies change with the speed of rotation (increasing speed to the right). Top row: near-perfect gases; bottom row: viscous fluids.

All of them are too small to exert much more than negligible tidal forces on their primaries.

Through theoretical hydrodynamic calculations the French mathematician Henri Poincaré had studied the effects of rapid rotation on any liquid mass other than a highly compressible gas. He found that if the rotation were rapid enough the body would be distorted into a pear-shaped object. The lower part of Figure 21, which does not pretend to quantitative accuracy, shows qualitatively the variations in shape to which such a rotating body is subject. Each figure exhibits the effects of more rapid rotations than does the one to its left. Darwin showed that if any additional force caused the smaller member of such a pair to revolve about the larger part more slowly than the latter rotated, tremendous tidal friction would result immediately. The neck of the hourglass would be severed with almost explosive rapidity and a satellite would be launched on a career similar to the one we have considered for the moon. In this situation the moon need not be of negligible size as compared to its planet, as in the case of the equatorial ring process. Thus no objection arose from the fact that our moon is far larger in comparison to its primary than is any other satellite in the solar system. Darwin concluded that the birth of our moon probably occurred in this manner and the astronomers of that time generally agreed strongly with him.

But apparently the earth never had the necessary moment of momentum to have carried the pear-shaped figure to the stage where the neck was constricted to a narrow bridge. Working backwards from today brought about equality of day and month while the two bodies still were **157** too far apart for tides to form the bridge. Darwin attempted the addition of what he called "tidal resonance" to bring about this stage where solar tides have separated the bodies. Later work by others showed that his additional effect, although present, was insufficient.

A moon formed in this manner through hourglass stages should move in the plane of the planet's equator just as a moon which evolved from the ring of equatorial particles. Darwin attempted to show from theoretical conditions how the present large angle between the planes of the moon's orbit and the equator of the earth might develop eventually.

The recognition of the lack of moment of momentum stimulated search for a substitute for Darwin's hypothesis. In 1951, G. P. Kuiper brought out a new form of evolutionary hypothesis for the planets of the solar system. He postulated centers of condensation which he called *protoplanets* in a flattened, rotating nebula with an early stage of the sun as center. The masses were larger than are the corresponding planetary masses today. If in one of the protoplanets there were two centers of condensation a satellite could form. Its mass might be large or small and it would not necessarily rotate in the plane of the planet's equator although there would be a tendency for that to be true.

Kuiper's hypothesis appears to most of us as the most promising which has been offered for the evolution of planets. We can guess that departures from it will consider only details. Also it seems to account well for evolution of satellites. However, our moon system is a freak and a hypothesis which fits the facts other places may not be the one which applies here. The main difficulty comes from the shape of the moon itself, as expressed by the *moments of inertia of its figure*. No satellite, unless it were surprisingly rigid, could be a perfect sphere. The tides of the primary must warp its shape and the nearer it be to that primary the greater must be the departure from sphericity. Our moon does not have exactly the shape that is demanded by tidal theory. It has been assumed that long ago it became rigid when the tides were greater than are those today and that since that time it has not kept pace with their changes. However, calculations have been made which indicate that there may never have been a time when it did conform. If this be true there can be only two possible explanations. The one is that there is a peculiar distribution of mass within it; the other that it has been a rigid body throughout the whole time that it and the earth have formed a system. Urey has attempted to meet the question by a very ingenious assumption that the surface has been loaded by meteoritic accretions of dense material since the time that it became rigid. His explanation well may be the true one. Unless it is accepted we must go to the always rigid moon. Such a body would be impossible under either Darwin's or Kuiper's hypothesis. The initially rigid moon would involve capture by the earth of an independent, small planet. The idea of such capture is a very old one but has been neglected since Darwin's time. The general idea has been worked out recently and appears to predict the general convulsive force needed to create the lunar maria, to explain their peculiar distribution, and to account for the lack of them on farside.[*]

Plate 18–1. Farside of moon as observed by the Russian Lunik III. The nearly vertical arc is the boundary between parts of the moon which we can see under the most favorable librations and those we can never see.

[*] For a more detailed exposition, see Alter, Dinsmore, Publications Astronomical Society of the Pacific, "The Evolution of the Moon," Vol. 75, Feb. 1961, pages 5–14.

19 LUNAR PHOTOGRAPHS

FROM SPACE VEHICLES

Until 1964 all pictures of the moon were taken from the earth. Since then, lunar observations have continued at an almost unbelievably accelerated pace.* In 1964 the first of the Ranger

* All of the United States vehicles designed to photograph the moon have been projects of the National Aeronautics and Space Administration, usually carried out by contracts with corporations or with research organizations. All were launched from Cape Kennedy. Except for the Orbiter series, the processing of data returned from space was through contract with the Jet Propulsion Laboratory of the California Institute of Technology. Lunar Orbiters I and II were under project management of NASA's Langley Research Center, Hampton, Virginia. Special thanks for courtesies in securing photographs and other data for use here are due to (among others) Dr. Homer E. Newell, Associate Administrator for Space Science and Applications, NASA; to Dr. W. H. Pickering, Director of JPL; to Dr. L. D. Jaffe, Surveyor Project Scientist, JPL; and to Dr. Thomas Vrebalovich, Division Representative Surveyor, JPL. The Luna IX photograph was obtained from a USSR press release in Moscow. For Orbiter II photograph, see page 70.

probe pictures were exposed. The Rangers were a series of rocket vessels designed to obtain photographs and other data concerning the moon's surface during the last minutes of flight before they were destroyed on impact. There were, in all, nine Rangers. The earliest of the series were entirely experimental, used to perfect the necessary techniques. Rangers VII, VIII, and IX were completely successful.

Each of them carried six cameras which were activated by command and which returned by television thousands of pictures during the moments before the destruction of the ship. The first pictures on each flight were secured at altitudes approximating 2,000 km. Below roughly 700 km the general detail shown of the surface began to surpass the finest exposed at our terrestrial observatories. Those which were obtained near the surface absolutely outclassed any of those obtained through the use of our greatest telescopes.

For two of the flights the chosen impact points lay on mare surfaces. For Ranger IX it was on the flattish central surface of Alphonsus, adjacent to Mare Nubium. These choices were due principally to the fact that such areas appeared to be better sites for the contemplated manned landings than are those in the rough mountainous regions. Landings from manned Apollos are expected to occur by 1969.

The Russians won the next great advance when one of their vessels made a semisoft landing on 1966 February 3 in Oceanus Procellarum. They secured about a dozen very valuable photographs of the surface surrounding the impact point. These pictures proved that the surface was solid enough to support such a vehicle. Previously, despite general belief that a ship would not seriously sink, the strength of the surface was merely a hypothesis. They also supported the conclusions from Ranger pictures that the mare surfaces, although pitted with numerous "rocks" and tiny craterlike depressions, are, in general, smooth enough to be used for moderately safe manned landings.

The third success was even more surprising than the first from Rangers VII, VIII, and IX. The successful vessel was the first of a series of a half dozen to be designated by the name Surveyor. No results, other than guidance toward technical improvements, had been anticipated. Its practically perfect success provided almost a pleasant shock to lunar scientists. The first proof that there had been at least a partial success was received instantly after impact by continuation of the broadcasting signals. The signals proved that a soft landing had been accomplished. This would have been sufficient to provide moderate satisfaction with the results of the project, even if pictures and other data had not been secured. Impact occurred at 1966 June 2^d 06^h 17^m UT. The landing mass was 280 kg. Impact was at $2°53S$ and $43°35W$.

Almost immediately after contact with the surface, scientists and technicians at the Jet Propulsion Laboratory began to question Surveyor about its condition and about the functioning of its many parts. Television carried the laboratory scene live to the whole of the country. The actions and expressions of the group, as the hundred replies were received, told, more emphatically than any report could have done, the full story of their great surprise. The responses in each of the many aspects showed a perfect success. If there had been men on the ship, they would have found the landing quite comfortable.

A few moments after impact, on order from the Goldstone tracking station in California, Surveyor began the transmission of the first of many thousands of television pictures, showing the immediate surface. Their quality was excellent, even in the "raw" condition that they first reached the recording instruments. Even after the cold of the long lunar night Surveyor continued to produce useful observations. After a few months when apparently it was dead, it revived sufficiently to transmit some data, although no more pictures.

Despite earlier failures, both the United States and Russia were successful during 1966 in placing vessels in orbit around the moon. The first of these was the Russian Luna X in April, followed in August by Luna XI, and in October by Luna XII. Although Luna X did send some information concerning radiation in space, some sort of difficulty, apparently, prevented accomplishment of any truly important mission. Luna XI, launched on August 24, was more successful. One of the excellent pictures of farside had been received from Zond 3 in July 1965 during a "flyby" which ended in orbit around the sun.

Orbiter I was launched from Cape Kennedy on August 10^d 19^h 26^m UT. It was placed in an orbit with approximately 1930 km apolune and 195 km perilune and with a lunar period of 218 minutes. One week after the first pictures were taken, the orbit was changed on command from earth to reduce perilune to 60 km. Its missions were to monitor space radiation, to determine meteoroid flux, to measure the form of the lunar gravitational field, and to photograph the surface, especially for the purpose of determining, accurately, the topography of nine sites which had been proposed for landing the first men on the moon. Because all of these were fairly close to the lunar equator a small inclination of $12°16$ was chosen for its orbit plane. These areas form a belt stretching from Mare Foecunditatis through Oceanus Procellarum. Observations of farside, extending by far the few Russian pictures, brought its study of that side also into the major program.

Orbiter II was placed in path around the moon on November 7 with somewhat the same missions. Because of the fact that Orbiter I had completed its missions and fear that it might interfere with proper reception of orders for Orbiter II, a change was made in its orbit to cause it to crash on farside.

Orbiter I carried two cameras, one with an 80 mm focal length and the other with one approximately $7\frac{1}{2}$ times as long. Each used three shutter speeds: $\frac{1}{100}$ second, $\frac{1}{50}$ and $\frac{1}{25}$ second. Unlike the Rangers and Surveyor, it used photographic film instead of live television. The Eastman film chosen was an aerial one having comparative freedom from fogging by space radiation. It was 70 mm wide and had a preexposed strip of data on one side. Orbiter carried a 60-meter roll of the film, sufficient for nearly 200 exposures by each lens. Exposed film was stored in a "looper" and was developed by an Eastman process called the "Bimat system." After development the film was stored and dried.

For transmission, the film was scanned by a light beam $\frac{1}{200}$ mm in diameter. The beam required 20 seconds to cross the field and, while doing this, made 17,000 transverse scans, each about 2.5 mm in length. Transmission was slow, and only two frames could be sent during one orbital transit.

All of the United States was saddened by the Apollo tragedy of 27 January 1967, which brought shock waves of realization of the fact that great achievements are usually gained at the expense of great sacrifices. But from the records of the past couple of years we can project our plans for the future. We *must* determine that our technology will do all that it can to safeguard the lives of individuals, without abandoning the great triumph of mankind. At the same time we *must* hold to a minimum the delay caused by the tragedy. We *must* perform even more frequent lunar missions, each of them with techniques improved from all past experiences. The next chapter tells why use of the moon presents the greatest opportunity which has been offered during the history of the race.

Plate 19–1. The shadow of Surveyor I on the moon. The background is a mosaic composed from many pictures exposed by Surveyor I.

Plate 19–2. Scale model of Surveyor I.

161

Plate 19–3. Ranger VII, camera A. Impact of Ranger VII, 1964 July 31^d 13^h 10^m 19^{s}60 UT. Exposed at 15^m 29^{s}22 before impact. Altitude at exposure, 1932.13 km. Scale, 200.7 km. (Consult Plate 3–20 for the general area.) The only large, explosive type of crater shown here is Bullialdus, which has a diameter of a trifle less than 60 km. Another important, but smaller, crater of the same type is Darney, which lies nearly 200 km directly north. Darney has a notable ray system. It lies almost on the southern shore of a small, oval-shaped mare which was named Mare Cognitum by the International Astronomical Union soon after the impact. Within the southern shore of this mare, and about 80 km to the left and north of Darney, is a moderately conspicuous, short ridge. Another similar ridge lies about 125 km directly north of this one. The impact point lies close to this second ridge. Later plates will show craterlets along the crest of each of these ridges.

Plate 19–4. Exposed at 5^m 35^{s}30 before impact. Altitude at exposure, 747.29 km. Scale, 78.7 km. The more open scale of this picture makes it comparable to the best ever made by the great telescopes of earth. Darney and the two ridges begin to show much detail. Just north of Darney is a large dome with several smaller ones in the general area. The presence of these smaller craters gives additional weight to the hypothesis that Darney was formed by internal forces, rather than by impact. (See Chapter 13.)

A line of small craters cuts the line which joins the ridges. Their system will dominate the pictures which are made at lesser altitudes. Many small, faint craterlets can be observed dotting the mare floor. One of these is shown on Plate 19–6 as being one of the most interesting objects of the lunar surface.

Plate 19–5. Exposed at 22.$98 before impact. Altitude at exposure, 53.82 km. Scale, 5.65 km. The line of craterlets mentioned in the previous plate dominates the central part of this one. The scale is about fifteen times more open. Most of the craterlets of the group form a wide open, inverted V. The pattern and the increased density of craters cannot be accidental. Some scholars believe that they were formed by impacts from a cloud of meteorites, possibly from the head of a comet. Another theory is that they were formed by internal forces, somewhat resembling terrestrial volcanic force. The diameter of the largest members of the group is less than one kilometer, barely observable from earth under the most favorable conditions. Two of nearly twice this size can be observed at the right border.

Plate 19–6. Exposed at 2.$50 before impact. Altitude at exposure, 5.85 km. Scale, 0.647 km. This is the final exposure made by camera A of Ranger VII. Impact occurred when the scanning was about nine tenths completed. The exposure of the videcon occurred 2.09 seconds before impact. It lasted for 0.$005 and the image was retained for the TV scanning, which is a 2.5-second process. The scanning began with a very narrow vertical line at the left of this picture and as each such line was completed, it moved slightly to the right till, after 1,150 such lines, the whole picture would have been transmitted. The altitude of the camera at the instant of exposure was 3,690 meters. The width of the scanned section is 1,360 meters and the diameter of the largest crater shown is about 225 meters, much too small to be observed from earth.

The largest crater in the lower right quadrant has a diameter of around 250 meters. On its floor several masses can be seen, one with a diameter of about 50 meters. Their nature is controversial and probably will not be known until man actually visits the area.

Plate 19–7. First of five plates from Ranger VIII. Exposed at 1965 February 20ᵈ 09ʰ 50ᵐ 45ˢ068 UT, which was 6ᵐ 51ˢ688 before impact. Camera A. Altitude at exposure, 753.79 km. Scale, 72.01 km. (Consult Chapter 15, pages 141–143.) This plate exhibits a marked appearance of diagonal lines from the lower right toward the upper left. Some able students have interpreted them as "gashes," cut by fragments of an asteroid assumed to have impacted on the area now known as Mare Imbrium. One of them, in the lower left portion of this plate, is discussed in some detail in the next plate. Near the center is Lade, a large hexagon-shaped walled plain, which has its two southern walls almost missing. Examination of Plate 3–11 shows that the missing walls lie within an alley of sunken terrain which extends from the vicinity of Hipparchus to pass just south of Julius Caesar.

Plate 19–8. Exposed at 3ᵐ 47ˢ368 before impact. Camera A. Altitude at exposure, 412.67 km. Scale, 41.45 km. Delambre is the large explosion type of crater seen at the top of this plate. D'Arrest, at the extreme lower right corner, is near the lower left corner of the preceding picture. In that picture it was seen as connected to Delambre by one of the "gashes." Before the Ranger pictures were exposed, no picture had an open enough scale to examine the details of this connecting line. Now careful study of its parts, with attention to their shadows, reveals that it is a series of ridges, rather than of valleys. Near the lower left corner is a pair of large craters: Sabine with its twin, Ritter, close on its lower right. Their floors are worth careful study.

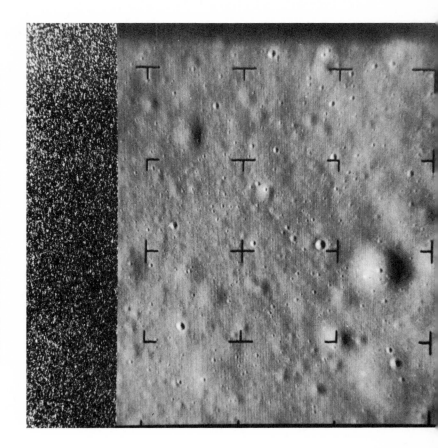

Plate 19–9. Exposed at 2.^s089 before impact. Camera A. Altitude at exposure, 3.69 km. Scale, 0.42 km. (The same comments about the data as given for Plate 19–6 apply.) The larger, shallow depressions, or craters, do not appear to be results of impact but rather to have resulted during the solidification of a once-liquid surface. There are, however, many sharp, tiny craterlets for which we do not have sufficient data to choose between the two hypotheses of origin. These tiny pores do not appear to be correlated to the first class. They may appear inside or between them. We can be confident that these smallest craterlets are a later formation than the larger type and came into existence after hardening of the surface. A few of them have bright halos, probably miniature ray systems. Possibly these are the youngest, but a hypothesis of impact by a meteorite of highest velocity appears to be as reasonable.

Plate 19–10. Exposed at 3^m 55.^s048 before impact. Camera B. Altitude at exposure, 426.84 km. Scale, 20.94 km. The large crater in the lower right corner is Sabine, which is described in Plate 19–8. The most important feature is the pair of nearly parallel rills which, beginning south of Sabine, extend diagonally across the picture. (Consult Plate 15–1 and the accompanying text.) The rills are among the broadest, and possibly shallowest, on the moon. Three short lines of craterlets enter the southern one from the south. Each ends exactly on a rill boundary. The idea has been advanced that these craterlets have been the result of meteoretic impact, "probably due to Theophilus" (Plate 3–7). Such a hypothesis appears to be untenable in this case.

Plate 19–11. Exposed at 25ˢ129 before impact. Camera B. Altitude at exposure, 44.59 km. Scale, 2.52 km. The length of this complex, peculiar feature is about 5 km. The southern end, quite definitely, is a craterlet, with a diameter of more than a kilometer. The lower end, less certainly, appears also to be one. However, it seems to have an axis more than 3 km lengthwise on the main feature. More probably this end also is an ordinary craterlet with another feature imposed on its northern wall. Outside the main features on both right and left are valleys approximately parallel to its main axis. There is an appearance, certainly illusory, of a veil lying over the central portion, leaving most of the two main craterlets uncovered. This "veil" reduced the albedo to that of the general background of the plate, without obscuring the smaller details. Probably the object is due merely to the chance association of unrelated features.

Plate 19–12. Ranger IX impact, 1965 March 24ᵈ 14ʰ 08ᵐ 19ˢ994. Exposed at 18ᵐ 36ˢ572 before impact. Camera B. Altitude, 2358.12 km. Scale, 97.84 km. This is the first Ranger IX photograph made with the 76-mm-focal-length TV camera. The altitude is not much less than the maximum for Ranger pictures. Alphonsus, within which lies the impact point, occupies the upper right corner. Several relationships to the larger Ptolemaeus are easily observable. Each is, approximately, a hexagon. They have one side in common. The floor of Alphonsus is divided in half by a ridge. The line of this ridge, if continued northward, becomes one of the walls of Ptolemaeus. A long valley, one of the most conspicuous of the so-called "gashes," runs southward from the lower right corner to merge with the inner part of the right wall of Alphonsus. It is important to notice that it is parallel to the Alphonsus ridge and to the right wall of Ptolemaeus. A line of craterlets, continuing the left northern wall of Ptolemaeus, merges with the corresponding wall of Albategnius. None of these relationships completely contradicts an impact hypothesis of their origin, but they are data that are hard to explain under it.

Plate 19–13. Ranger IX, camera A. Impact of Ranger IX, 1965 March 24ᵈ 14ʰ 08ᵐ 19ˢ994. Exposed at 1ᵐ 35ˢ13 before impact. Altitude of exposure, 226.61 km. Scale, 23.05 km. (Consult Plates 3–19 and 16–1.) The crater Alphonsus fills nearly the whole of the picture. Unlike such craters as Tycho and Copernicus that brighten very much under a high sun, this one disappears except for the famous black spots along its principal rill (Chapter 12 and Plate 6–1). Probably Alphonsus is a vast caldera, formed simultaneously with Mare Nubium, which borders it on the right. The northern half of its central ridge is seen to be very low. The bright central mountain differs in appearance from all others on the lunar surface. The left half of the floor exhibits some very prominent rills, usually lined with craterlets. The right half shows none (see page 138).

Plate 19–14. Exposed at 1ᵐ 42ˢ812 before impact. Camera B. Altitude at exposure, 244.59 km. Scale, 10.40 km. Plate 19–13 showed several important rills on the left floor. The greatest of them is shown in detail on the right side of this plate. Even a glance demonstrates it to be so fully lined with craterlets that it must lie along a fault to which the craterlets are intimately related. All the rills on the Alphonsine floor exhibit this relationship more or less strongly. The phenomenon cannot be the result of impacts. The cause must lie within the lunar surface, at least partially. The left-hand side of this plate is composed of the mountain system which lies outside Alphonsus. When the crests of the ridges are examined carefully, it is common to find them lined with craterlets. Perhaps the most conspicuous example is the one lying near the upper left corner. The relationship is too strong to be the result of chance. It is impossible to explain it by any meteoritic hypothesis. On the other hand, it must be remembered that these mountains may be considered as the outermost parts of the Alphonsus wall. Perhaps if we had equally open-scale pictures of mountain systems far from any large craters we might not find such craterlets.

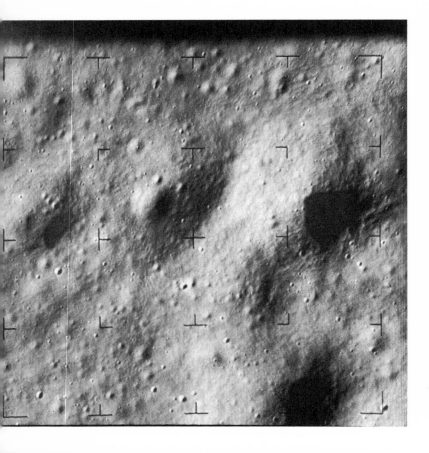

Plate 19–15. Exposed at 5ˢ532 before impact. Camera B. Altitude at exposure, 13.39 km. Scale, 0.57 km. This is the last complete frame which was exposed by the Ranger IX longer-focus camera. Impact occurred very soon after exposure of its next picture. The width of the whole scene is only little more than 2½ km. The tiniest recognizable of the hundreds of craterlets are merely a few meters across. The largest of the depressions has a diameter of about 1½ km. It covers much of the area to the right of the center, and is so irregular in shape that it would be improper to speak of it as a crater. The largest of the true craters lies almost at the middle of the left edge, and has a diameter of approximately a half kilometer. Inside of it is a line of three conspicuous craterlets. Craterlets with diameters near fifty meters are very common, and a fairly definite line of them crosses the whole picture, just below its upper edge. In general, the picture suggests the solidified surface of a former boiling viscous fluid. It is probable that some of the smaller craters were formed by meteoritic impact, although the data are too few for any certainty.

Plate 19–16. Exposed at 0ˢ412 before impact. Camera B. Altitude at exposure, 1.0 km. Scale, 40 meters. This photograph was made with the most open scale of any lunar photograph before Luna IX and Surveyor I. Impact occurred when only a tenth of the frame had been scanned, resulting in a picture with only a 22-meter east-west width. The "large" crater at the bottom of the picture has a diameter of less than 20 meters. The three next largest are approximately half this size. The smallest observable are a mere half of a meter. The best Surveyor pictures show "pores" which are much smaller. There is a strong tendency, near the middle of the photograph, for the craterlets to line up along diagonals from lower left.

Plate 19–17. This is one of the earlier pictures exposed by Luna IX. The extremely rough appearance is due to the fact that the sun was very close to the horizon and the shadows were very long. To the left of center, on the bottom edge of the picture, one of the "petal" tips is visible. Above it is a stone of perhaps 15 cm diameter. Its shadow length is at least several times its height. Still higher is another stone which actually may have a greater diameter. Beyond it is a crater which extends more than halfway across the picture. On the horizon above it is another stone. The picture shows numerous black lines, possibly similar, on a tiny scale, to the rills which can be observed from earth (pages 137–138). In the foreground are many tiny features which appear on this picture to be tiny craterlets, down to diameters of less than a centimeter. However, some of them may be merely shadows of small stones. Due to the fact that chemical, instead of solar, batteries were used, no pictures were received after February 4. The height of the camera above the surface was estimated as near 60 cm. It was rotated about an axis that was tipped somewhat toward the horizon, in order to secure a panoramic series of pictures. The mass of Luna IX which impacted was about 100 kg. Under the astrographic convention the lunar coordinates of the impact point were 7° north and 64° west.

Plate 19–18. Part of Surveyor I landing pad and nearby lunar surface. Each of the three legs on which Surveyor I landed had a shock absorber on which the initial impact force, the slight rebound, and the final weight pressure were recorded. From their records and from examination of photographs, such as this one, it was learned that the surface at the impact point was a slightly cohesive agglomeration of particles usually less than a millimeter in size but larger than fine dust particles. It is estimated that the footpads sank between four and eight centimeters below the surface, rebounded slightly, then settled into final position. The surface gave evidence of a slight compression and showed that some material was pushed out from the impact depression. This picture was exposed on June 4, using the 100-mm camera focus when the solar altitude was 54°, sufficient to prevent shadows from gentle slopes. Surveyor carried no general experimental apparatus, merely photographic, plus those sensors which were needed to secure data about itself. However, especially with regard to lunar surface temperatures, these did furnish some additional data. The camera was equipped with a variable-focus lens with extremes of 25 mm and 100 mm, usually employed at one or another of these limiting values. This picture is a "narrow-angle" frame with a width of 6°.4.

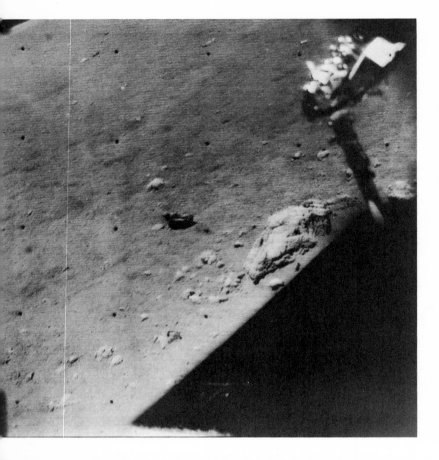

Plate 19–19. This picture is a "wide-angle" frame (25°) exposed on June 6. The bottom is in the shadow of Surveyor, but extending upward are the housing for some temperature-sensitive equipment and one of the omnidirectional antennas. (See picture of the Surveyor model, with callouts of the principal parts.) Just above the shadow is a lunar rock, located about 4 m from the TV camera. Its height above the surface is about 15 cm, and its length is three times that value. Near it are more than a dozen smaller rocks with sizes ranging to perhaps 10 cm. Their distribution indicates that there is a genetic relationship to the larger rock. Other rocks are observable in the background, but because their distances are uncertain, their diameters are unknown. The edges of the principal rock are rounded, indicating but not proving that it is the result of solidification from a liquid. A short section of the horizon is visible in the upper left corner of the photograph. The black dots which are arranged at regular intervals over the picture have exactly the same fiducial purposes as the similarly placed short lines of the Ranger pictures.

Plate 19–20. This picture made by Surveyor on the morning of June 5 shows primarily the area to the east (astronautic convention) and slightly south of the vehicle. In general it is a slightly rolling plain with numerous rocks scattered over it. The distance to the horizon is unknown, but has been estimated as several hundred meters. The largest rocks are at the horizon, near the upper left corner. These must be a meter or so in width, far larger than the one observed in Plate 19–19. Also close to the horizon and a little to the right of these rocks is a small complex feature, part of which looks like a pile of rocks. Farther to the right, a little below the horizon but closely parallel to it, a greater density of rock numbers can be followed across half of the picture. At first glance it appears to be a rather broad line. However, study indicates it to be complex, with a regularity which would not be expected through mere accident. Such lines of stones have been interpreted by some of the most able students, who have had the opportunity to study all of the thousands of pictures, as being the outer rims of craters. Tentatively this description should be accepted. Their estimated diameters range from a few meters to perhaps a hundred.

Plate 19–21. This picture should be studied in connection with Plate 19–20, which shows a somewhat similar but less distinct and more irregular line of rocks. Even in the original picture the contrast of this one was much the greater, but, in addition, the picture has been processed by use of the computer in order to exhibit the maximum detail possible. The following quotation is from a preliminary study: "Line of large rounded blocks in foreground mark the rim of a large ancient crater several hundreds of meters in diameter. The far rim of the crater can be seen on the horizon." The rim would seem to be more pronounced and regular than one would expect it to be for such a crater, but every other explanatory guess appears to offer more difficulties. We need more data!

Plate 19–22. This magnificent mosaic of the lunar surface to the south of Surveyor is composed of many narrow-angular frames, exposed at a low solar altitude in order that the shadows should bring about maximum detail of craters and rocks. The center of the picture is southwest of the camera. They were trimmed to fit by a skillful artist and were mounted on a glass sphere. A small part of the vehicle shows at the bottom. The serrated edge is due to the fact that the line connecting a feature of one frame to one on another, which is at the same distance from the camera, is not parallel to an edge of the frame. Reversal of the directions of shadows is primarily a result of their different directions from the camera. The shadows actually are quite closely parallel because there was little change in the sun's position during the time that the group was exposed.

Plate 19–23. "The man in the Earth." The following is NASA's press release concerning this picture: "The world's first view of the Earth taken by a spacecraft from the vicinity of the Moon. The photo was transmitted to Earth by the United States Lunar Orbiter I and received at the NASA tracking station at Robledo de Chavela near Madrid, Spain. This crescent of the Earth was photographed August 23 at 16:35 GMT when the spacecraft was on its 16th orbit and just about to pass behind the Moon. This is the view the astronauts will have when they come around the backside of the Moon and face the Earth. The Earth is shown on the left of the photo with the U. S. east coast in the upper left, southern Europe toward the dark or night side of Earth, and Antarctica at the bottom of Earth crescent. The surface of the Moon is shown on the right side of the photo." Three simple facts must be remembered when looking at such a picture. The phase of Earth as seen from Moon is exactly the reverse of Moon's phase as seen from Earth. The appearance of Earth depends not only on the positions of continents and oceans but also on the seasons and the size and severity of its storms. The surface of Earth always will be more or less blurred by the effects of even a clear atmosphere.

Plate 19–24. On first examination of this photograph it appears to be a view of an ordinary region of the moon's mountainous areas. However, upon realization of the scale, we see that the implications are different. The width of the picture approximates 1350 km and the length 1500. The circular crater near the southern edge has a diameter of nearly 400 km. This is larger than that of any similar feature on nearside. Even Clavius and Deslandres are dwarfed by it. It is larger even than some of the smaller maria of nearside, for example Mare Humboldtianum. Just to the north of this giant, and slightly to the left, is a curved scarp with a rather flattish area at its base. The principal part would give the impression of being part of an immense ringed plain. On its left the ring is completely interrupted by a line of five moderate-sized craters. To their left is a quite large, typical ringed plain. Between the scarp and the 400-km crater is a small, deep, ringed plain with a central mountain. Whatever may be the cause of ringed plains, it must be a process which sometimes can be interrupted before completion. (See Chapter 12.) We can guess that this area is primarily the result of endoforces, not of impacts, although probably there were many small ones.

Plate 19–25. This plate from farside must rank among the most important photographs of lunar features. The area is located at 146° east (astronautical convention) longitude, well around toward the point which commonly is farthest from what is visible on earth. The picture approximates to 80 km in width and almost 95 km, north and south. The larger of the two principal craters has a diameter of about 40 km, the smaller of 25. Superficially, at least, the pair resemble Alphonsus and Arzachel. In this case there is no need to avoid a definite statement that both have, in the main, resulted from endoforces and that each is primarily a caldera. (Plate 16–1.) The larger exhibits a long rill which is nearly parallel to the inner base of its rim. Like the corresponding rill in Alphonsus, it contains small craterlets. A low central ridge crosses the floor as in the case of Alphonsus. At the extreme north and left of the floor there is a short, heavy rill, similar to those on the floor of the smaller southern companion. The floor of the southern crater shows more rills and wider ones than, possibly, any other lunar crater. We can be certain that at one time it was completely molten. After this it solidified and was acted on very strongly by one or the other of two forms of endoforce. Possibly the still-molten interior formed craters from below as in the case on the island of Mauna Loa, which exhibits also the reverse case where the lava has been drained away, causing cracking and collapse of the solidified surface.

Plate 19–26. The width of this plate is approximately 1080 km and the north-south diameter 1280 km. Like Plate 19–24 it is located on farside. The first object to catch the eye is the immense walled plain which carries also some of the characteristics of a ringed plain. (See crater plains in glossary.) Its diameter is roughly 330 km. The sun was 20° above the horizon at the center of the plate. It was exposed on August 25. Plate 19–24 was exposed earlier on the same day. Perhaps the object worthy of the most study is located just below the middle of the southern edge of the picture. It is quite definitely a ringed plain, the central part of which was molten at some past time. Halfway between it and the right-hand edge is a scarp which is centered on this ring. Apparently there was some general sinking which was insufficient to melt the surface except at its center where a strong local subsidence created this plain. It is smaller than Mare Nectaris and the related Altai Scarp but the resemblance is sufficient to indicate the same sort of origin. (Consult page 93.) There could be no criticism if the I.A.U. should decide to consider it as being one of the smaller maria. Its diameter approximates 230 km.

Plate 19–27. In this farside picture, exposed August 26, a larger and later-formed crater, on the right, breaks into a smaller one. Almost always, as would be expected under pure chance, a smaller intrudes on a larger. At first glance quite a number of interesting details demand explanation. However, upon further study, it becomes evident that in most cases a second picture, with the sun shining from the left, must be studied before much confidence can be placed in guesses. The long history of study of lunar features has many examples of hypotheses published too quickly. The northern part of the rim of the smaller crater is broken, and, apparently, dark molten material flowed southward through the gap onto the floor. This hypothesis is intriguing, and if the crater was formed soon after general solidification of the area, that action may have disrupted the lunar surface farther north and brought about such a flow. At the extreme left there appears to be a valley which is almost parallel to the edge of the plate and which is too wide to be designated as a rill. There is no intrusion on any part of the rim of the larger of the pair. Probably the smaller crater is primarily the result of endoforces, but at present a guess as to the origin of the other would be dangerous.

Plate 19–28. This picture exhibits a valley which, on a smaller scale, resembles the Alpine Valley so closely that their causal forces must have been of an almost identical nature. (Consult Plate 15–6 and page 141.) This photograph is about 40 km square. The length of this valley approximates a fifth that of the other. The center of the plate is at 30° 45′ west (astronautic) and 1° 30′ north. The low altitude of the sun, 12°, exaggerates the effects of shadows, and therefore causes the surface to seem rougher than it is. The valley is in the general area within which the impact of Ranger VII occurred, about 12° north of that point. Each valley passes through a hilly region but has both of its ends in or near a mare type of the surface. It certainly is a graben.

20 MAN ON THE MOON

The reasons that impel the United States and presumably the Soviet Union to undertake to land men on the moon are many and varied. Perhaps the most immediately compelling considerations are those of power politics and international prestige, but these need not concern us here. The fact is that the moon is there and the means to reach it are within men's reach. Unless the drive to explore and discover is forcibly restrained, men will reach the moon sooner or later. What good will it do?

There may be indirect military advantages for a nation that controls the moon, but such a nation would already have great satellite, space ship, and space station capabilities, and occupying the moon would not in itself add much to its power. There may be economic rewards, but this is highly speculative and even unlikely. There will surely be great scientific gains. The moon must be used as a vast high-vacuum laboratory for physicists, a nearly pristine record of past ages for the geologist, a shining new field of discovery for many other investigators. Above all, it will be a magnificent new observatory site for the astronomer, where he will be able to use his telescope for studies he would not dream of attempting from beneath the turbulent sea of air that wraps the earth.

The difficulties involved in colonizing the moon should not be insurmountable. Man should be able to protect himself and accomplish useful work in the lunar environment although it does seem probable that his real home will remain the earth!

Men making a preliminary visit to the lunar surface will use their small space vessel as a place to live until their return. What they can do outside the vessel will depend largely upon what is learned about the smoothness or roughness of the surface. It may be that they can walk about protected merely by suits somewhat similar to those used by high-altitude aviators today. Perhaps they will first explore the surface in tracked vehicles. It may be that the roughness of the surface will necessitate a special type of vehicle that will not travel on the surface at all but will hop from one point to another. The choice between these methods of travel will have to depend upon observations we cannot make from the earth.

Eventually the time will come to settle down in semi-permanent stations. One likely site for such a settlement on the rocky lunar surface would be a small crater-like depression. Such a craterlet if properly roofed would offer maximum protection against the temperature changes of the month and would be relatively invulnerable to meteoritic bombardment. It would also provide a partial necessary radiation shield. It should be rather easy eventually to roof over such craterlets in a way that would be almost impossible of accomplishment on earth. The small weight of a domed roof should make easy installation possible; the air pressure inside the living quarters should support the whole weight. Above the roof dome there would have to be a second thin roof to protect the interior from solar radiation, which would otherwise at times beat upon the quarters with an intensity beyond human endurance.

Within the first small craterlet "village," man can relax and live somewhat as he does on his home planet. If this first experiment is successful, larger craterlets will be prepared for village sites. Lines of craterlets such as exist in the vicinity of Copernicus may be useful. One would guess that because of safety conditions and engineering difficulties it is unlikely that any large crater will be prepared for habitation. "Cities" very probably will be entirely unknown.

During the first few weeks of living on the moon it will be necessary to use supplies brought from the earth. In order to reduce to a minimum the mass of supplies that must be transported, air and water will be recycled and purified, and vegetation grown on the rocket itself may supply much of the food. If it should prove to be impossible eventually for man to obtain his sustenance from the moon itself, little could be done on its surface other than to make the scantiest and quickest of surveys. Indications are, however, that the moon can be made self-sustaining for a race which has great scientific and technical knowledge.

We can be fairly confident that gases quite similar to those in the earth's atmosphere escaped from the rocks of the satellite in the early days of the moon's history. In one or two places there are lunar valleys that may have resulted from ancient water erosion. If this actually was the case it does not mean that the moon once had a supply of surface water, but merely that in some tremendous volcanic action water vapor was brought up from interior rocks, condensed, and then poured down the mountainside in one cataclysmic torrent. If this happened, the water quickly evaporated and the molecules escaped into space. With sufficient power and with

our knowledge of chemistry and physics we should be able to secure the necessary water and air from the rocks themselves.

The power, at least, should be no problem, because of the high daytime temperature. At the subsolar point the temperature is just above the boiling point of water as we experience it at sea level on the earth's surface. Tubes containing water or other suitable liquid, blackened to cause maximum absorption, could be mounted in cylindrical reflectors parallel to the moon's axis and turned very slowly to follow the sun.

By this means the sun can act as a perpetual fuel source for lunar steam engines or generators. As much power as may be desired for any engineering work will be available through the ages at practically no cost except that of the first installation. But an even simpler source is at hand. The continuing improvement of solar cells that convert radiant energy directly to electricity gives reasonable hope for even more convenient power supplies. This would enable man to accomplish engineering and chemical engineering projects he could never hope to undertake on earth. The problem of electric power during the long nights would be solved by storage batteries or by nuclear batteries.

Hopefully man will use the moon solely as an international laboratory for basic scientific research. The most exciting prospect one can see at this time is in astronomy. The moon is an ideal site for an observatory. Astronomers at the surface of the earth cannot possibly use their telescopes with any great efficiency; as a matter of fact it is really surprising that in three and a half centuries they have been able to do as much as they have. The reason for this is simple enough: we live at the bottom of a great ocean of turbulent air. At sea level there is a column of air weighing 15 pounds above each square inch of the surface. As we rise above sea level we rapidly leave more and more of this atmosphere below us until after only a few miles it is much too thin to support life. At a height of a little more than six miles, $\frac{4}{5}$ of the earth's atmosphere is below us. At 18 miles only about $\frac{1}{25}$ of the air still remains. Traces of air have been observed by means of aurorae at heights of about 600 miles, but at 1,000 miles, for all practical purposes, no air remains.

This ocean of air absorbs roughly one-half of the incoming radiation from the sun and from other objects, and in particular it absorbs almost all of the very short-wave (or high-frequency) radiation. This is in itself an extreme handicap to the astronomer, but it is not the worst of the story. The worst problem is turbulence. Our air is composed of various components or masses continually moving and mixing at different temperatures. Air at one temperature and density bends light passing through it differently from air at another temperature and density. The result of this hodgepodge is that all objects in space appear to tremble; the twinkling of the stars is a simple illustration. Telescopes magnify this shimmering effect as much as they do the objects under view. Even under the best conditions at such places as Mount Hamilton, Mount Wilson, Palomar Mountain, and Kitt Peak, this effect is always very serious.

Because of these innate disadvantages it will be well to consider the potentialities of an observatory located on the surface of the moon and the advantages that may be derived from it in our effort to learn the organization of the physical universe. The list of advantages given below is extremely incomplete, for there is no point at which some benefit will not be apparent for an observatory.

In considering the problem of observation from the moon, there must be an understanding of the ideal image of a star as it is formed by a telescope. A star is a large body of highly heated gases quite similar to our sun, which happens to be a very ordinary star. But the other stars are so far away that even the very largest and closest of them are little more than points of light in the sky. Our telescopes cannot magnify them; the best that we can hope for here is well-defined, discrete points of light. Betelgeuse and Mira have diameters as observed from the earth of about $\frac{1}{20}$ of a second of arc—an angle less than $\frac{1}{1000}$ of the angle measurable by the ordinary engineer's transit. If a point source of light is viewed under ideal conditions through a telescope having a one-inch objective or mirror, it will seem to have a disk $4\frac{1}{2}$ seconds of arc in diameter.

The diameter of this spurious disk limits the resolving power of the telescope. Resolving power is inversely proportional to the telescope's aperture or mirror size. The smaller the disk the better. If a ten-inch telescope is used this spurious disk has a diameter of only $\frac{45}{100}$ of

a second. A 100-inch telescope reveals a disk just about the size of the actual disk of the stars Betelgeuse and Mira. The 200-inch telescope, under ideal conditions, should give us a spurious disk about half the size of the real disk. The central star images on photographic plates exposed through large telescopes should theoretically appear as very small round dots. But because we observe all stars only through our atmosphere, this theoretical image is distorted and blurred, and appears larger than it should. There also is a small but continuous shifting of its position in random directions during the exposure of the photographic plate, further diffusing the image. On the moon, by way of contrast, the images will be as perfect as the optics of the telescopes that produce them.

The accuracy of star definition is important for many investigations including fundamental observations of the distances of stars. These are obtained by photographing the nearer stars against a background of the more distant ones at time intervals of about six months. During these half-year periods the position of the earth has been shifted by 186,000,000 miles by reason of its orbital motion around the sun. As we look at a nearer star from these two opposite sides of the orbit, it appears to have moved its position slightly with respect to the more distant stars behind it. The star's apparent shift from its mean position is called its *parallax*. For Alpha Centauri, the closest of all stars, the parallax is about three-fourths of a second of arc. Very serious errors in the measurements of these small angles, and therefore in distance calculations, result from the fact that the images vary in apparent size because of atmospheric distortion. If we could secure nearly perfect images, our measurements of parallaxes would be much more accurate, and we could carry our direct measurements of distance to a far greater number of stars. Our whole scale of distances in the universe depends upon these fundamental measurements. On the moon, where the amount of atmosphere is negligible and conditions are always ideal, we would obtain a far more accurate fundamental scale of distances.

Light gathering power is also important in the observation of the less luminous dwarf stars within our own galaxy. This was one of the main purposes for which the 200-inch Hale telescope was constructed. Just as there are stars that give many thousands of times as much light as our sun there are also those that give many thousands of times less. These are the faint dwarfs, and of course they can be observed only at relatively short distances—on the order of 50 light years at most. There is still no way of observing from the earth the fainter dwarf stars in the more distant parts of our galaxy, although the 200-inch telescope doubled the distance at which these could be photographed and therefore gave us eight times the volume of space as a sample from which attempts can be made to extrapolate the laws of stellar distribution.

Because of the almost perfect images that will be formed when a telescope is used on the moon, all the light from a star will be concentrated on a smaller area of the plate and will therefore blacken it in a shorter time. Moreover, with no atmosphere to absorb stellar light, the stars will appear about twice as bright as they do on earth. Finally the long nights and the very important absence of atmospheric glow in the night sky will make possible photographic exposures many times longer than on earth. The net result of these three factors will be the observation of dwarf stars much farther from the sun than any that can be seen at present. Even if the maximum distance visible were to be multiplied by as little as ten times, a sample 1,000 times greater than is available from the earth would become accessible.

On the moon, observation of binary stars will also be much more effective. These are pairs of stars that move around each other as a revolving system. Some of these binaries are far enough apart so that even a small telescope will separate them readily, but the separation between many others can be observed only with a large telescope. In many cases the components appear too close to each other to be separated at all. The ideal observing conditions provided by the moon will make possible the separation of many pairs much closer than those we now distinguish. The lunar vacuum will also make the observation of angular distances between the components more accurate, thereby improving data on the orbits of all binaries. All of this will add materially to our understanding of stellar evolution, a subject about which we know far too little.

Even the weaker gravitational attraction on the moon will be an important advantage. The largest refracting telescope in the world, the 40-

inch at Yerkes Observatory, just begins to exhibit a distortion of images as the result of objective bending under the earth's gravitational pull. The 200-inch mirror at Mt. Palomar has been made very thick and is supported at many points by a very complicated lever system in order to prevent bending that would distort the stellar images. The tubes of telescopes also bend under their own weight, and expensive special construction is the unfortunate but necessary result. At the surface of the moon, where objects weigh only one sixth as much as on earth, there will be far less distortions of stellar images due to flexure in the telescopes. And because telescopes there will be much lighter in weight, they will also be easier to handle and less expensive to construct.

New planetary detail will be observed from the moon. The same blurring of images that interferes with our terrestrial observations of stars applies to each point on the surface of a planet. Mars, for example, when it is closest to the earth, has an apparent diameter of 25 seconds of arc. Each second corresponds to about 160 miles of the planet's surface. Since the resolution of a 10-inch telescope is such that it spreads a point of light over about $\frac{1}{2}$ second of arc, it spreads light from any point on Mars' surface over roughly 80 miles, or a circle 40 miles in radius. The result is fuzziness of detail even if the observing conditions are ideal. With the 100-inch telescope, each point is spread over an area with a radius of about four miles. The 200-inch telescope at Palomar, with a resolving power of about $\frac{1}{40}$ second should theoretically bring in really fine details of the surface. But the distortion from our atmosphere diffuses the image greatly and we can see only a small fraction of what we might hope to find. There is the further fact that large telescopes suffer far more from atmospheric distortion than small ones do. The percentage of nights on which the whole aperture of the 200-inch can be used advantageously for observation of fine detail is much less than for moderately sized instruments. On the moon this obstacle to the efficient use of large telescopes will not exist. Astronomers have estimated that a 300-inch reflector is probably the largest telescope that can ever be practical for use on the earth because of this increasing difficulty with the atmosphere. On the moon, if cost and engineering problems can be surmounted, a 1,000-

inch telescope can be used as continuously as a small one.

Today there is great uncertainty whether free oxygen exists in the atmosphere of Mars. The spectrum of Mars or of any other planet must be observed through the atmosphere of the earth, which is much denser than that of Mars and produces the same absorption lines we are attempting to observe in the planetary atmosphere. The oxygen lines from the two planets are superimposed. A spectral line from Mars is, however, not completely indistinguishable because Mars is usually moving either toward us or away from us. Because of the Doppler shift that this motion causes, its spectral lines shift slightly either to the right or to the left of those produced by our own atmosphere. The shift is very small though, and there is a tendency for the strong lines from the earth's atmosphere to obscure any attributable to Mars. On the airless moon, however, very accurate spectral analysis of the composition of planetary atmospheres will be possible. This, however, is one of a few matters which should be settled by use of spectrographs on our artificial satellites even before we get to the moon.

Study of the sun's corona, or faint outer layer, will be more effective from the moon. On earth these studies are best advanced during total solar eclipses, when the moon hides the entire bright surface of the sun from a small area of the earth. During an eclipse the far fainter outer atmosphere or corona of the sun can be observed protruding beyond the hidden disk of the solar photosphere. Under unusual conditions the corona has been observed to extend more than 10,000,000 miles from the sun's disk. But even during the best of eclipses the earth's sky is rather bright, and the astronomer must observe the faint, pearly streamers of the corona against a background of such light. Naturally a great deal of detail is lost. A quarter of a century ago Dr. Lyot of France invented a complicated instrument called a coronograph, which obscures the photosphere so that the corona can be observed from mountain tops and other unusually good locations even without the occurrence of an eclipse. These observations, however, are not nearly so satisfactory as those made during an eclipse. On the airless moon the sky is black even during the daytime. A very simple form of the coronograph, used principally to keep extraneous light away from the photographic plate or other sensor, will produce observations of the coronal streamers far more satisfactory than those obtainable here at any eclipse. The fine details can be followed hour after hour, for periods extending through the long lunar day. With details of coronal changes observed continuously, and with its spectrum uncontaminated by terrestrial light, the manner in which the coronal atoms radiate or scatter light can be studied much more satisfactorily. The streamers of the corona will be followed much farther from the sun than would ever be possible on the earth, and possible segregations of various atoms in different outer regions of the corona can be looked for.

Our atmosphere interferes with the passage of other than visual radiation, of course. It seems reasonable that the short-wave solar radiation absorbed by the atmosphere must influence our weather far more than do the forms of radiation to which our air is almost transparent. This short-wave radiation includes ultraviolet and probably extends to frequencies beyond those described as x-ray radiation. From the moon the solar spectrum will be observed under perfect conditions, already hinted at by the advances secured from spectrographs carried by rockets. If there is to be any hope of long-range weather prediction for the earth it seems probable that it must come in part through daily study of the sun's ultraviolet radiation.

One of the most important observations made by astronomers concerns the brightness of stars, and these too will be more effective from the moon. Relative stellar brightnesses are measured with great accuracy by the use of modern electronic methods in conjunction with telescopes. But there is a complication. As a star rises from the horizon toward the zenith, its light passes through less and less of our air and we get a spurious change in its brightness. Allowances must also be made for the varying transparency of the atmosphere even at a constant altitude and during a very clear night. The changes, moreover, are not the same for all wavelengths of light. The observer of the brightness of stars must correct all his observations for all of these changes, and since the corrections can never be applied perfectly they increase the uncertainty of the results. On the moon very tiny variations in the intensity of radiation from a star will become rather easily observable, and photometric measures will have an accuracy to which terrestrial results can scarcely be compared.

On the moon the astrophysicist will be able to penetrate obscuring galactic clouds of very thin gas and dust more efficiently than he can here. Although some of these are so nearly transparent that stars can be observed through them from the earth, especially by use of infrared light, the apparent luminosities of the stars decrease in the process. The blackness of the lunar sky will increase the possible length of photographic exposures made from the moon; this, in combination with the improved images of the stars previously described, will permit observation of more stars through these thin galactic clouds, to the great benefit of the astrophysicists.

Finally, from the moon we will see far deeper into remote space. Perhaps the greatest observational program of the last half century has been devoted to the study of external galaxies, systems varying from large ones like our own with 100,000,000,000 stars or more to dwarf galaxies comparable to the largest clusters within our galaxy. The observation of these galaxies was the chief purpose for which the Hale telescope was constructed. But exposures with this great instrument and with the 48-inch Schmidt are limited due to the fogging of the plates by the light of the night sky. If the background were truly black, the increased length of exposure should show much fainter galaxies than can be found today. The contrast between a faint galaxy and a truly black sky would also help much in revealing them.

With the Hale telescope galaxies have been photographed so remote in space that light has reached the telescope more than 2,000,000,000 years after it left the distant stellar system. But yet more distant galaxies must be observed to clarify the still mysterious nature of time and space. Relativity has taught us that they are quite different from what they were once supposed to be; it seems possible, for example, that in some sense space curves back on itself. The oldest stars in our region of space seem to have originated perhaps 20,000,000,000 years ago. Our sun is about 6,000,000,000 years old. Some of the most luminous of the stars were born only a few million years ago. Many answers would be provided if we could photograph galaxies far more distant and therefore fainter than those that can now be brought into view. For example, are there galaxies that existed 40,000,000,000 years ago, or did our universe come into existence more recently?

The astronomer is particularly bemused when he contemplates the possibilities of one specific observation that could be made from a lunar observatory. This would be a high dispersion spectrogram of one of the more distant of the galaxies observable in the black * sky of the airless moon, and would require a large reflecting telescope comparable to the greatest on earth today. It is just possible that such a telescope may be available there within 100 years. The combination of that sort of telescope with a spectrograph of high dispersion is used now to make the most intimate possible study of the nature of the brighter objects, but exposure times must often be measured in hours before the photographic plate is blackened sufficiently for the radiating atoms and molecules to tell all they can about conditions on the target. But when the time comes for the great observation from the moon, an astronomer using the powerful telescope under conditions of perfection will make a spectrogram with a truly long exposure time.

If we are to have any hope at all of really understanding the general nature of our physical universe, questions of this kind must be answered not by mathematical speculation alone but primarily by definite and precise observations. There is little hope of enlightenment from this side of the moon. Man must force his way to its inhospitable surface, carrying with him the localized environment to make continued existence there possible, and the curiosity and skills and tools to enable him to initiate the great work of discovery. Those who have faith in the human race feel certain that this will be done, and increasing numbers believe that occupation of the moon will be an achievement of this century. What man does on the moon will be merely the prelude to what he will do later. Humanity stands almost at the threshold, ready to cross into a new age of exploration.

---

* Commonly we speak of the lunar sky as black because most of it so appears to the human eye. However, much special radiation comes from it: cosmic radiation, radiation from interplanetary plasma, solar wind, zodiacal light, solar corona, Milky Way background.

APPENDIX

LICK OBSERVATORY PHOTOGRAPHS

With the exception of some of the photographs made to correct for limb foreshortening, all lunar pictures exposed before 1954 were part of the Moore-Chappell series made at the Lick Observatory during the years 1937–1947 with the 36-inch refractor. During this interval it was customary to notify Dr. Moore and Mr. Chappell whenever seeing conditions were unusually good and the moon was available. They would make several exposures, then return the instrument to the regular observer for the night. Lunar and planetary photography requires unusually steady seeing conditions. Many nights that are quite satisfactory for spectroscopic work, for example, would be wasted if given over to this type of program. A plan such as this is the only efficient one to use.

Each of the Moore-Chappell photographs covered the whole of the moon. As a result, they were used for all general atlas types of work. The refractor is handicapped, of course, by lack of complete correction for chromatic aberration. For this reason all of these Lick photographs were limited to the yellow-green region through use of a suitable filter. Most of the exposures were on Kodak Solar Green spectroscopic plates. Exposure times, depending on phase, varied from 0.1 to 1.2 seconds.

The cooperation of Dr. C. D. Shane, former director of the observatory, is much appreciated. He made it possible to study each of the negatives in detail and furnished transparencies of all for which further study was desired. In all this Mr. Chappell assisted wholeheartedly. Not only did he make superlative transparencies but he gave valuable technical advice.

MOUNT WILSON AND PALOMAR OBSERVATORIES

All of these photographs were made by the author as guest observer through the courtesy of the director, Dr. Ira S. Bowen. Between April, 1954, and March, 1959, 478 negatives were made. All were exposed at the Cassegrain focus of the 60-inch reflector at Mt. Wilson. Because of the difficulty of removing very heavy spectrographic equipment, the plates used were not large enough to cover the whole of the moon. The program was primarily a color-index examination for any significant differences between exposures made in the blue-violet and the infrared. One pair of such plates, exposed in the most rapid possible succession, composed an observation. In the earlier exposures one of these was a IIa-0, but in the later a II-0 was used. Both were used without filter and depended on the plate cutoff near $\lambda = 4900$. The earth's atmosphere interfered much less with the infrared photographs than with the shorter-wave ones. As a result they were used for all plates here except for the few cases in which comparison of a pair was desired. Except where otherwise noted, all were developed in a rocking tray for five minutes in D 19 at a temperature near 70° F. Nearly all of the infrared plates were Kodak 1-N, exposed through a Pyrex CS 7-69, CG 2600 glass filter, which has its 10% cutoff near $\lambda = 7200$. In a few cases, slow, fine-grained and contrasty IV-N plates were used near full moon phase in order to emphasize shade differences between rather large areas of the floors of maria. The same filter was used for them. Continuation of these observations is contemplated. It would have been very difficult to have prepared these pictures for study and for enlarged reproduction without the expert assistance of Mr. Paul E. Roques of the Griffith Observatory. A photograph of the moon is necessarily underexposed at the terminator and overexposed in other areas. If a print is to exhibit any large area to the public, this difference must be corrected. But if the original negative is ever to be used for even qualitative photometric research, it must not be modified. Mr. Roques met the problem by silhouetting skillfully while making enlarged transparencies and duplicate negatives.

CORRECTION OF LIMB FORESHORTENING

Before World War II Dr. Fred E. Wright of the Carnegie Institution of Washington, assisted by his son, Dr. F. H. Wright, developed a technique for correction of foreshortening of lunar features near the limb. He had the Eastman Kodak Company coat some fairly large glass globes for use as photographic plates. Next he projected a photograph of the moon on a matte-surface, white globe of the same size as the glass globes and focused very carefully. The image on the globe reversed the foreshortening and revealed features in almost their true form. Then he carefully substituted for the white globe one of the sensitized glass globes—in effect a spherical photographic plate—and exposed it. The developed picture showed the moon almost as it actually is. The optical planning was difficult and even the exercise of great care could not prevent defects at the limb.

Two of the seventeen Wright globes were loaned to the Griffith Observatory for public exhibition. In 1954 it occurred to the author to copy these globes from points directly over features of especial interest in order that pictures of the true forms could be available to a larger audience. Mr. Roques cooperated and we were fairly successful. Then, using the 40-inch parabolic mirror removed from the center of the 200-inch telescope, we began projecting plates onto white, wooden globes and copying directly. Some of these pictures are reproduced in this book. They show certain features almost as we would see them from a rocket almost directly overhead.

Later some still better projections were made at the University of Chicago by Dr. Harold C. Urey, who made them available for use here. All of these pictures emphasize how different the apparent forms of limb features are from their true ones, making incorrect interpretations very frequent.

Table 6. Lunar data

Some of the following lunar data are given in greater detail than usually will be desired, but the user should have little difficulty in choosing a proper rigor.

MASS

In tons	8.0×10^{19}
In grams	7.32×10^{25}
In terms of earth's mass	0.01226
In terms of sun's mass	0.0000000368

DIAMETER

Miles	2160.
Kilometers	3476.
In terms of earth's mean diameter	0.27227
Mean geocentric, angular	31'07"

SURFACE GRAVITATION	
In terms of earth's	0.165
In feet per second per second acceleration	5.31
In cm per second per second acceleration	162.

VELOCITY OF ESCAPE AT SURFACE	
In terms of earth's	0.213
Miles per second	1.48
Kilometers per second	2.38

DENSITY, MEAN	
In terms of water	3.33
In terms of earth's mean	0.6043

TEMPERATURES OF SURFACE ROCKS	
Sun at zenith	214° F, 101° C
Night	−250° F approx.

MAGNITUDE	
Mean of full moon	−12.5

ALBEDO	0.07

AVERAGE LENGTH OF MONTHS

	d
Synodic	29.530588
Sidereal	27.321661
Draconitic (nodical)	27.212220
Anomalistic	27.554550
Tropical	27.321582

LIBRATIONS, MAXIMUM	
Geocentric in longitude	7°54′
Geocentric in latitude	6°50′

FRACTION OF SURFACE	
Always visible	41.0%
Sometimes visible	18.0%

ORBIT (data are those of Professor E. W. Brown)

Distance	
maximum	252,710 miles
minimum	221,463 miles
mean	238,860 miles
Parallax, mean	57′02″.54
Inclination of orbit plane to ecliptic, mean	5°08′43″
Inclination of orbit plane to earth's equator	
maximum	28°35′
minimum	18°19′
Inclination of moon's equator to ecliptic	1°35′
Inclination of equator to orbital plane	6°44′
Eccentricity, mean	0.0549

Mean velocity in orbit	
Linear, miles per hour	2,287; km 3,680
Angular, per hour	33′

REGRESSION OF NODES	
Period of	18.5995 years
Annual change	19°.341

ADVANCE OF LINE OF APSIDES	
Mean period of	8.8503 years
Annual change	40°.690

THE COLONGITUDE OF THE SUN

Space travel is giving this subject an increasing pragmatic value. It is not difficult except for the fact that the conventions which have been adopted are rather "sticky." The colongitude is merely the trigonometric complement of the selenographic longitude of the sun. That longitude of the sun equals the longitude of the point on the moon's surface for which the sun is in the zenith. We must remember that, with respect to space, the earth and the moon rotate about their axes in the same direction. We must remember also that, as seen from the north pole of the moon, longitude is measured in a counterclockwise di-

Figure 22. Colongitude of the sun. The circle is the moon's equator. *P* is the point which we on earth see as the mean center of the moon's visible disk. It is located in Sinus Medii. Its selenographic longitude and latitude are zero.

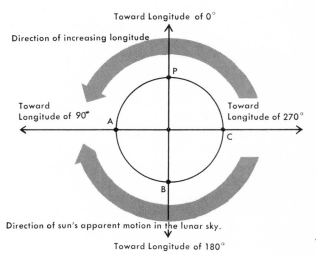

Toward Longitude of 0°

Direction of increasing longitude

Toward Longitude of 90°

Toward Longitude of 270°

Direction of sun's apparent motion in the lunar sky.

Toward Longitude of 180°

rection. As watched from this same point the sun appears to move around the moon in a clockwise direction. This causes the selenographic longitude of the sun to change in a negative direction. The colongitude of the sun equals 90° minus the selenographic longitude of the sun. Negative values are avoided by adding 360° where necessary. In the diagram the moon is seen from a point over its north pole. The circle is the moon's equator. P is the reference point for which both the selenographic longitude and latitude equal zero. The direction of the moon's rotation is shown by an arrow. The other arrow shows apparent motion of the sun with respect to the moon.

When the sun is rising at P its longitude is 90°. Therefore its colongitude is zero, which equals the longitude of P. When it is noon at P the longitude of the sun is zero and the colongitude is 90°. When it is sunset at P the longitude of the sun is 270° and the colongitude is —180°, which changed by 360° gives the tabulated 180°.

Colongitude is useful for determining noon at a greater distance from the moon's equator than for determining sunrise and sunset. The obvious reason for this is the variation in length of time the sun is above the horizon as we go to higher latitudes.

The I.A.U. has now reversed the convention for east and west on the moon insofar as selenonautical maps are concerned. For astronomical use it has advised a use of right and left instead of east and west.

TRANSLATION OF LETTER RECEIVED FROM N. A. KOZYREV

"I am sending you prints of the three most interesting spectrograms of the Crater Alphonsus which I obtained on November 3, 1958. The slit of the spectrograph was oriented as shown in the diagram.

"Spectrogram 1) Nov. 3, 0^h to 1^h UT. You will notice that the central peak is redder than the neighboring background and has a normal appearance of the spectrum.

"While guiding there was noticed an unusual decrease in brightness. Probably at this time the central peak was illuminated by the sun and was shining through the ejected gas. [Note: on Plate

16–2 this spectrum can be seen at the bottom.]

"Spectrogram 2) Nov. 3, 3^h to 3^h 30^m UT. The spectrum of the central mountain shows a bright gaseous emission. The most prominent emission bands are the 4756A (which has not yet been identified), and the group 4735, 4713, 4696A —the Swan bands of the molecule C_2. There are also Swan bands 5165, 5130. One sees clearly the group of bands C_3 of comet spectra between 4100 to 3950A. In addition, one can see many other bands; their identification has not yet been made. [Note: on Plate 16–2 this spectrum is at the top.]

"Spectrogram 3) During the guiding of the spectrogram 2 I noticed a marked decrease in the brightness of the central region and an unusual white color. All of a sudden the brightness started to decrease. At this instant the exposure was stopped and a new one was started from 3^h 30^m to 3^h 40^m. The result was a normal spectrum (there was only a slight suspicion of the Swan band 4757).

"The luminescence of the ejected gas was excited by the hard radiation of the sun which could penetrate only into the outermost layers of this cloud of gas. Hence the emission could be observed only above the little mountain, very slightly displaced (approximately one second of arc) in the direction of the sun. It is interesting that in the region of the brightest emission bands 4757–4735–4713, the shadows are deeper than in those portions of the spectrum where there are no bands. This shows that the optical thickness of the molecules of C_2 was greater than one; hence the process of the ejection of gases was of considerable magnitude and there could have been noticeable changes of the crater.

"I would be greatly interested in knowing whether you succeeded in photographing Alphonsus on December 1–2 as you intended. I should be grateful if you would send me copies of these photographs and also prints of your previous photographs of Alphonsus. If it is not too difficult, please send me also your articles on the nature of the lunar surface.

"Your remarkable photographs of Alphonsus, obtained through filters, convinced me that there exist luminescent clouds of gas in this crater. As a result of this, I started systematic spectrographic observations of this crater. Your work was the first which has demonstrated the possibility of gaseous emanations on the moon."

GLOSSARY

ABSOLUTE ZERO: about 273° below zero Centigrade. At this point the normal motion of molecules, which decreases in speed with decreasing temperature, would cease completely.

ACHROMATIC REFRACTOR: see *Chromatic aberration.*

ALBEDO: the fraction of the light which a body reflects of that which falls on it.

ALTITUDE: the angular height of an object above the true horizon as measured along its vertical circle.

ANGULAR DIAMETER: the angle subtended by the actual diameter of an object as seen by an observer. Angular diameter varies inversely with distance; at twice the distance the angular diameter is half its former value. The angular diameter of the moon varies during the month from 33′30″ when closest to us to 29′21″ when farthest.

ANGULAR MOMENTUM: see *Momentum, moment of.*

APOGEE: the point in its orbit where the moon or an artificial satellite is farthest from the earth. Opposite of *perigee.*

ARGON: a heavy gaseous element that is found in small quantities in the terrestrial atmosphere (A). It is colorless and tasteless.

ASTEROID: a synonym for *minor planet:* any planetary body that is smaller than a regular planet but large enough to be observed.

ASTRONOMICAL UNIT: the mean distance between the centers of the earth and sun. It is close to 93,000,000 miles.

ATMOSPHERE: the gaseous envelope that surrounds an astronomical body. It includes the molecules of water vapor, but not the dust particles.

ATMOSPHERIC ABSORPTION: the absorption of a variable amount of the radiation that enters the air. Our air is not perfectly transparent. The absorption is greater at the blue end of the spectrum than at the red end.

ATOMIC FISSION: the breaking of an atom into lighter atoms and subatomic particles. It is accompanied by the release of intense radiation.

ATOMIC FUSION: the building of heavier atoms from those of less mass. It is the process by which the sun produces its radiant energy. In this case, on the sun, helium is formed from hydrogen.

AURORA: light emitted by the thin upper atmosphere of the earth at heights roughly between 50 and 600 miles. Auroras are caused principally by charged hydrogen particles and by electrons from the sun.

AXIS: the line through the center of mass of a body, about which it rotates. The poles of rotation are the ends of the axis, where it cuts the surface of the body.

AZIMUTH: the angular distance measured westward from the south point of the horizon to the point on the horizon directly below an object (*i.e.*, at the foot of the object's vertical circle). Engineers commonly measure azimuth either east or west from the north point instead of the south point.

BINARY: a physical double star; that is, two stars that are close together and move in ellipses around their mutual center of mass.

BLACK BODY: a body that absorbs all the radiation that falls on it and reflects none. Strictly, no object is a black body. But the moon, sun, planets, and stars approximate black bodies, and it is convenient to consider them as such in order to determine their temperatures by their general radiation.

BLINK-TYPE SCANNER (or microscope): a device in which two photographic transparencies may be adjusted side by side for examination through an eyepiece. The light that passes through them to the eyepiece is interrupted rapidly, coming from one picture for an instant, then from the other. If the photographs are exactly alike, the observer sees no change, but if some small area or object exists in only one of the pictures, or is in a changed position, or is of a changed brightness, he sees a conspicuous jumping effect instantly.

BLOWHOLE CRATER: a form of small volcanic crater found on the earth. Some of the lunar craterlets may be quite similar to them.

CALDERA: a type of volcanic crater which has been formed primarily by a sinking of its floor rather than by the ejection of lava.

CAMERA LUCIDA: a prism (or mirror) device at the eyepiece of either a microscope or a telescope, by means of which the observer sees an enlarged image on a white screen beside and below the eyepiece. This enables him to trace the enlarged picture.

CELESTIAL EQUATOR: the great circle in which the plane of the earth's equator cuts the celestial sphere. See also *Equatorial plane*.

CHROMATIC ABERRATION: the failure of a lens to bring all wavelengths of light to focus at the same distance. This produces a colored halo around the image. The fault can be partially corrected by making the lens from two or more pieces of glass of different densities. Such a lens is called *achromatic*.

CLEFT: see *Rill*.

COLONGITUDE: the lunar longitude of the sunrise terminator. Colongitude is more nearly accurate than phase for indicating the position of the sun relative to the moon because it has been corrected for the moon's librations. The *American Ephemeris* gives these values for each day.

COMET: a body of extremely low mass and density but often with a volume thousands of times that of the earth, moving in an eccentric orbit around the sun. Most of the material is in the "head," which probably is composed mainly of meteoroids and gas. Many comets have long gaseous "tails."

CONJUNCTION: the position in which one body of the solar system is most nearly in line with another, as seen from the earth. For example, the moon is in conjunction with the sun at the instant of the new moon.

CONTINENTAL SHELF: that part of the floor of the ocean near the shore of a continent and shallower than the general floor. It is bounded by a scarp which may approximately parallel the continental shoreline. Similar areas are found on the floors of some of the lunar maria.

CONTINUUM: as used here, the continuous background of light in the solar (stellar) spectrum.

CORONA: usually the outer atmosphere of the sun which, during a total eclipse, looks like a crown around the new moon. The word may be used to describe any phenomenon that looks like a ring surrounding an object.

CORONAGRAPH: an optical device by means of which it is possible to observe the corona when the sun is not totally eclipsed.

CRATER: in lunar studies, any depression of the moon's surface other than a valley. The depression may have been caused by chance or by impact of a meteorite or an asteroid; or it may be a volcanic crater or a *caldera* (sunken area). The term *endocrater* is coming into use to denote any crater that has resulted from internal causes. *Ectocrater* has been suggested for any crater thought to have been formed by external causes. However, *impact crater* covers this group quite well.

CRATER CONE: the hill, often steep, that a volcanic crater may build about itself.

CRATER PIT: a very small craterlet.

CRATER PLAINS: the largest lunar craters are divided into two general classes: (a) the explosive *ringed plains* with their external walls and (b) the *mountain-walled plains* with little or no external walls.

CRATERLET: any lunar crater that is less than approximately five miles in diameter.

CRATERS, EXPLOSIVE: craters which appear to be results of violent explosions. They exhibit definite outer walls. These craters may be either endo-craters or impact craters or possibly, in the case of certain large ones, hybrids between the two.

DAY, APPARENT SOLAR: the interval of time as measured by the sundial between successive passages of the sun across the meridian.

DAY, LUNAR SIDEREAL: the sidereal day on the moon, a time interval equal to the sidereal month.

DAY, LUNAR SOLAR: the solar day on the moon, a time interval equal to the synodic month. It varies slightly.

DAY, MEAN SOLAR: the average length of the apparent solar day throughout the year—24 hours.

DAY, SIDEREAL: the interval of time between the passage of a star across the observer's meridian and the next passage of the same star. It is approximately 3 minutes 56 seconds shorter than the mean solar day, and is the true period of rotation of the earth on its axis.

DIAPHRAGM: an opening that restricts the passage of light through an optical system.

DISPERSION: the separation of light into its component wavelengths (or colors) by a prism or a grating.

DIURNAL: daily.

DOME: a low rounded elevation on the moon. It may be as much as ten miles in diameter and perhaps as little as 50 to 200 feet high.

DRACONITIC MONTH: see *Month, nodical.*

DWARF STARS: those stars that have a luminosity comparable to that of our sun, or less.

ECCENTRICITY: the measure of the departure of an ellipse from circularity. A circle has an eccentricity of zero.

ECLIPSE: (a) the passage of one body into the shadow of another. In a lunar eclipse the full moon passes into the shadow of the earth. If it enters completely, there is a *total lunar eclipse;* if not completely, a *partial lunar eclipse.* (b) If the new moon completely hides the sun as seen from any point of the earth, there is a *total solar eclipse.* For this to occur, the moon must be at a point in its orbit where its angular diameter is greater than that of the sun. If conditions are right for a total solar eclipse, except that the moon appears smaller than the sun, there is a thin ring of the sun seen around the moon. This is an *annular eclipse.* If the new moon does not completely block the sun from view for any point on the earth but does hide part of the sun, there is a *partial eclipse.* Often total and annular solar eclipses are called *central eclipses.* The *eclipse year* is the interval of time the sun takes to move around the ecliptic from one of the moon's nodes to the same one again. The eclipse year is about 346.62 days long.

ECLIPTIC: the great circle of the celestial sphere around which the center of the sun travels in the course of the year. Also the great circle in which the plane of the earth's orbit, extended, cuts the celestial sphere.

ECTOCRATER: see *Crater.*

EJECTA HYPOTHESIS: the hypothesis that lunar rays, and some other phenomena, are the result of solid bodies ejected from a lunar crater.

ENDOCRATER: see *Crater.*

ENDO-EXPLOSION: an explosion resulting from causes within the moon.

ENDO-LUNAR: from within the moon.

EQUATORIAL PLANE: the plane through the center of mass of any body and perpendicular to the axis of rotation of that body.

EQUATORIAL TELESCOPE: a telescope that is fitted with machinery that causes it to follow a star without readjustment. The rotation of the earth causes all stars to appear to revolve around the earth each day in paths that are parallel to the celestial equator.

EQUIPARTITION OF ENERGY: equal division of energy. A gas acts very much as though it were composed of small elastic bodies. These particles continually strike each other and rebound. Two that have done this will have the same energy as a result. Because of the countless collisions, all the particles in a gas tend to have the same energy of motion. See also *Absolute zero.*

ERG: the metric unit of energy. One erg equals the energy of motion that one gram of matter has when moving one centimeter per second. It is a very small unit.

ESCAPE VELOCITY: the outward velocity needed for an object to escape from a celestial body.

FAULT: a fracture of the surface, along which there has been slippage, either vertical or horizontal.

FILTER: in astronomy, a substance which permits certain wavelengths of light to pass through but which stops all others.

FORESHORTENING: distortion in two-dimensional view of a sphere—objects near the edge appear crowded together in the radial direction.

GALVANOMETER: a device for measuring electric currents.

GEOCENTRIC DIAMETER: the angular diameter of the sun, moon, and planets as measured from the center of the earth.

GHOST: the bare hint which remains of a lunar feature that has been practically destroyed by some later action.

GLOBE-PROJECTION METHOD: a photographic process by which most of the foreshortening of lunar photographs can be corrected. See also *Foreshortening*.

GRABEN: a sunken area between faults. Opposite of *horst*.

HALF-CRATER: a feature that appears to be the remaining half of a partly destroyed crater.

HELIUM: the next to the lightest of the chemical elements (He). It is the end product of the sun's energy-generation process.

HORIZON, TRUE: the great circle in which a plane perpendicular to the plumb line of the point under consideration cuts the celestial sphere. Each point of the surface of the earth or moon has a different true horizon.

HORIZONTAL REFRACTION: the amount that an object which is at the true horizon appears to be raised toward the zenith because of the refraction of light by air. Under standard conditions horizontal refraction equals 36'29".

HORST: a surface area cut by faults. Opposite of *graben*.

HYDRODYNAMICS: the study of the laws of motion and action of liquids.

IMPACT FORMATION: a crater or other feature that has been formed by impact of a meteorite or asteroid.

INCLINATION: (a) the angle between two planes or, sometimes, the complement of this angle. For example: the inclination of the plane of the moon's orbit to the plane of the ecliptic is 5°08'. (b) Sometimes, when one of the planes is the equator of a body, the context makes it more convenient to tell the same fact as the inclination of the *axis of rotation* toward the second plane. For example: the obliquity of the ecliptic usually is defined as the angle of inclination of the earth's axis of rotation toward the plane of the ecliptic. It is 23°27' at the present time.

INFRARED: electromagnetic radiation of wavelength too long to be seen by human eyes but too short to be detected by radio equipment. We observe it by means of its heating effect and by use of special photographic plates.

INSOLATION: the total amount of radiative energy from the sun received at any given place during a specified interval of time. It depends on the intensity of radiation and the length of time that it is received.

INVERSE-CUBE LAW: relationship affecting tidal forces, which decrease, approximately, as the cube of the distance of the disturbing body. If our moon were twice as close as it is, the tidal force would be about eight times as great.

IONIZED PARTICLE: an atom or molecule that is electrically charged.

ISOSTASY: the condition under which the weight of a column from the center of a body (such as the earth or moon) weighs the same as every other such column. If the body is not rigid, this condition is imposed on it automatically by its gravitation, its rotation, and any other steady forces. If, however, it is rigid, the strength of its material prevents its conforming to changes in the forces and there may be a lack of isostasy.

ISOTHERM: a locus of points that are at the same temperature. Isotherms are printed on the daily weather maps in many of our newspapers.

KINETIC ENERGY: energy of motion of any body. It depends directly on the mass of the body (doubling the mass doubles the kinetic energy), and on the square of the speed (doubling the speed increases kinetic energy four times). See also *Absolute zero*.

KRYPTON: one of the gaseous elements found to a slight extent in our air (Kr).

LATITUDE: the angular distance measured from the equator along a meridian.

LIBRATION: usually the real or apparent oscillation of the moon that allows us to see some of the hidden side; sometimes the oscillation of other celestial bodies.

LIMB: the "edge" of the disk of the moon, sun, or a planet as it appears from the earth.

LINE OF APSIDES: in the case of the orbit of the moon, the line connecting *perigee* and *apogee*.

LONGITUDE: angular distance measured around the equator. On the moon it is measured from the center of the visible disk when all librations are zero, counterclockwise as seen from the north.

LUNAR TIDE: a very slight bulging of the moon due to the tidal force of the earth on it.

MAGNETIC FIELD: the distribution of force around a magnet. The moon has little or no magnetic field.

MARE (*plural* maria): any of the large, dark areas on the moon or Mars. Because the earliest observers believed such an area to be a body of water, they named it "mare," which is Latin for "sea." Apparently lunar maria are tremendous plains of lava with a thin covering of dust.

MASS: the amount of material that composes a body.

MERIDIAN: any great circle that passes through the poles of rotation of a body. All meridians are perpendicular to the equator of the body.

METEOR: the flaming light observed during the passage of a solid body traveling at high speed through the earth's atmosphere from outer space. See also *Meteoroid*.

METEORITE: a meteoroid that has landed as a solid on earth. See also *Meteoroid*.

METEOROID: a solid body moving in orbit around the sun but too small to be observed from earth.

MICROMETER: a device for measuring very small lengths or angles.

MOLECULE: the smallest particle of any chemical substance. Breaking up the molecule changes the substance.

MOMENT OF INERTIA: a measure of the "resistance" of a body to changes in its rotation.

MOMENTUM: the product of the mass of a body by its velocity.

MOMENTUM, CONSERVATION OF MOMENT OF: when two bodies are moving around their mutual center of mass (for example, the earth and moon), their total moment of momentum is a constant unless some other body interferes.

MOMENTUM, MOMENT OF: the product of the momentum of a body by its distance from any chosen point around it which is desired.

MONTH, ANOMALISTIC: the interval required for the moon to pass from *apogee* (or *perigee*) to the same point again. It is important in distinguishing between predictions of total and annular solar eclipses. Its length is 27.55455 days, slightly longer than the sidereal month, because of a slow forward motion of the apogee.

MONTH, CALENDAR: one of twelve unequal intervals into which the civil year is divided.

MONTH, NODICAL: the interval required for the moon to pass around its orbit from one node to the same node again. It is essential in eclipse predictions because the new, or full, moon must be rather close to a node for any kind of eclipse to occur. Its length of 27.21222 days is slightly less than the sidereal month because of a regression of the nodes around the ecliptic.

MONTH, SIDEREAL: the interval required for the moon to pass around its orbit until it again reaches the same place with respect to the stars, as seen from the earth. This interval amounts to 27.32166 days.

MONTH, SYNODIC: the interval from new moon to new moon. It averages 29.53059 days.

MORPHOLOGY: as applied to the moon, a study of the kinds of features on it, their sizes, causes, structure, and changes.

MOTION: the process of changing place or position. *Linear motion* is the rate (e.g., number of kilometers per second) an object moves with respect to another object chosen as origin. *Angular motion* is the angle on the celestial sphere passed over in some arbitrary unit of time—as, for example, 13° per day eastward around the path of the moon's orbit. *Direct motion* is the eastward direction in which the earth moves around the sun. All planets have direct motion around the sun. However, some satellites move in *retrograde* orbits (from east to west) around their primaries. *Proper motion* is the slow change of a star's position against the stellar background because the star is moving in space. For most stars this motion is only a fraction of a second of arc per century.

MOUNTAIN-WALLED PLAINS: see *Crater plains*.

NADIR: the point on the celestial sphere through which a plumb line would pass if extended downward; it is exactly opposite the *zenith*. Since no two places on the earth have the same plumb line, each location has a different nadir and zenith.

NEWTON'S LAW OF GRAVITATION: each particle of matter in the universe attracts each other particle with a force that is directly proportional to the product of their masses and inversely proportional to the square of the distance between their centers.

NIMBUS (*plural* nimbi): the appearance of a halo or cloud around a feature.

NODE: one of the two opposite points where great circles intersect each other. In astronomy, usually one circle is the *ecliptic* and the other is the circle traced on the celestial sphere by the orbit of the moon, a planet, a comet, or an artificial satellite. The *ascending node* is the point where the object passes the ecliptic from south to north; the *descending node* is the reverse point.

OCCULTATION: the hiding of a body by a much larger one.

OPPOSITION: a position halfway around the celestial sphere from the body of reference. For example, the full moon is in opposition to the sun.

ORBIT: the path of a body around another. The path can be predicted from the law of gravitation.

ORBITAL PLANE: the plane that contains the orbit of an astronomical body.

OUTGASSING: the escape of gas from a solid or liquid.

PANCHROMATIC EMULSION: photographic material that is sensitive to all wavelengths (colors) of light in the visible spectrum.

PALUS: Latin for marsh. A lunar area that looks like a terrestrial marsh.

PARABOLIC MIRROR: a concave mirror having a parabolic surface. Such a mirror will produce far better images of distant objects than a spherical mirror.

PARALLAX: the apparent shift in position of a celestial body against the background of stars, caused by a shift in position of the observer. From the amount of shift, the distance of the celestial body can be calculated.

PERIGEE: the point in the orbit of the moon (or of an artificial satellite) where it is closest to the earth. Opposite of *apogee*.

PHASE (LUNAR OR PLANETARY): as applied to the moon, usually the length of time since the last "new moon" phase. For planets usually the ratio of lighted to total surface as seen from the earth.

PHOTOMETER: any one of various devices for measuring the intensity of a light source.

PHOTOSPHERE: the lowest level that we can see into the sun. It looks like a surface in our telescopes and photographs. Most of the sunlight comes from the photosphere.

PLUME RAYS: rays, especially of the Copernican system, that look somewhat like feathers. The "feather" points toward the primary crater.

POLARIZED LIGHT: light waves that have been made to vibrate in a particular direction.

POTENTIAL ENERGY: energy due to position, as contrasted to *kinetic energy*. A weight held above the floor has potential energy. If it is released, the potential energy is transformed into an equal amount of kinetic energy. See also *Kinetic energy*.

PRISM: a transparent solid or liquid (usually glass) bounded by plane sides (usually three) that can change the direction of a light ray or separate a ray into its component wavelengths, giving the band of color called the *spectrum*.

PROTOEARTH: a probable early form of the material that became the earth. According to one hypothesis, the material from which the moon was formed was part of the protoearth.

PROTON: one of the elementary particles that make up atoms.

PROTOPLANET HYPOTHESIS: the hypothesis that the sun was a nebula with a mass greater than it has at present, and that there were various secondary centers of condensation revolving around the center of the nebula. These secondary centers were the protoplanets. See also *Protoearth*.

RADIATION: the form of energy that travels through space at a speed of about 300,000 km. per second. Depending on the wavelengths, it is divided arbitrarily into radio, infrared, light, ultraviolet, x-rays, and gamma rays.

RAY SYSTEM: the bright streaks radiating out from certain of the moon's ringed plains and smaller craters. They become conspicuous under a high sun.

REFLECTING TELESCOPE (REFLECTOR): a telescope in which a concave mirror instead of a lens forms the image of the object to be observed. See also *Refracting telescope*.

REFRACTING TELESCOPE (REFRACTOR): a telescope in which the image of the object to be observed is formed by refraction of light passing through a lens. See also *Reflecting telescope*.

REFRACTION: the change of direction of light as it passes from a transparent medium of one density to one of a different density. Prisms and lenses use refraction to produce the desired results.

RILL: a narrow valley on the moon. See also *rima*.

RIM CRATER: a small crater on the rim of a large craterlike formation.

RIMA: Latin for a rill. Officially adopted by the International Astronomical Union in 1961.

RINGED PLAINS: any of the larger craters of an explosive origin.

ROCHE'S LIMIT: the minimum distance apart that two bodies can exist in stable condition. If they are closer together, the mutual tidal forces will disrupt one or both bodies.

SATELLITE: any astronomical body that revolves around another of much larger mass. The word usually refers to moons, that is, bodies that revolve around the planets.

SAUCER: a saucer-shaped depression in the floor of a mare or of a mountain-walled plain.

SCARP: a cliff or a line of cliffs.

SEAWARD WALL: the part of the wall of a shoreline crater that is toward a mare. Usually it is lower than the remainder of the wall and it may be entirely missing.

SELENOGRAPHIC LONGITUDE: the angular distance measured from the mean center of the moon's visible disk, as seen from the earth, along the moon's equator to the foot of the meridian through the object.

SELENOGRAPHY: the study of the surface of the moon. The lunar equivalent of terrestrial geography.

SELENOLOGY: the general study of the moon and its nature.

SENSOR: a device for detecting radiation. Among the common sensors are photographic plates, radio receivers, bolometers, thermocouples, masers, and the human eye.

SIDEREAL: pertaining to the stars.

SOLAR BATTERY: a device that converts solar radiation directly into electrical energy.

SOLAR DAY: see *Day*.

SOLAR TIDE: the part of the ocean tides which is caused by the sun. The solar tides are a little more than a third of the lunar ones.

SOLAR WIND: the outward streaming of electrified particles from the sun. The winds are continuous although varying in intensity.

SPECTROGRAPH: an instrument, usually attached to a telescope, used to photograph the spectrum.

SPECTRUM: (a) the band of colored light into which a light ray is separated by a prism or a diffraction grating. (b) the series of wavelengths that are emitted by a luminescent gaseous element. No two elements emit the same series.

SPECULAR: mirrorlike.

SPHERICAL ABERRATION: the failure of a spherical mirror to bring to a common focus point all the light from any one point of the light source. This defect is corrected by substitution of a paraboloid mirror for the spherical one. Lenses also have spherical aberration.

SUBSOLAR POINT: the point on the surface of the earth, moon, or a planet for which the center of the sun is at that instant exactly at the zenith.

SUBTEND: literally, "to extend under." Used with respect to the chord of an arc of an angle. If the angular diameter of the moon is 31 minutes of arc, the moon becomes a chord of that angle and we say that the moon subtends an arc of 31 minutes.

SWAN BAND: a series of wavelengths emitted by a molecule composed of two atoms of carbon. It is commonly found in the spectra of comets.

TERMINATOR: the great circle on the moon that is the boundary between day and night. We speak of the sunrise and the sunset terminators. One-half of the circle is always visible from the earth.

THERMOCOUPLE: a very sensitive and accurate electrical device for measuring temperature. It consists of two dissimilar materials (metals or semiconductors) joined together. Heat absorbed by the joint is directly converted into electricity. The temperatures of points on the moon are measured with a thermocouple set at the focus of a telescope.

ULTRAVIOLET: electromagnetic radiation of wavelengths shorter than the eye can see.

VERTICAL DIAMETER: the diameter of the lunar or solar disk which, at a given instant, is in a vertical position.

WALLED PLAINS: see *Crater plains*.

WANE: to become smaller. The visible lunar disk wanes during the interval from full moon to new moon. See also *Wax*.

WAVELENGTH: the distance between successive crests (or troughs) of a wave.

WAX: to grow larger. The visible lunar disk waxes from new moon to full moon. See also *Wane*.

X-RAY RADIATION: electromagnetic radiation that lies within a certain region of wavelengths much less than those of ordinary light.

XENON: a colorless, tasteless, gaseous element that is found in very small quantities in the earth's atmosphere (Xe).

ZENITH: the point where the plumb line, prolonged upward, cuts the celestial sphere. See also *Nadir*.

INDEX

193